Prese ᴎ ᴇrs

(

Including Ν ⌐..⌐ɾʋft

DestinWorld
publishing

First Edition 2018

ISBN 978-1-9997175-2-0

© 2018 Destinworld Publishing Ltd

British Library Cataloguing-in-Publication Data
A catalogue record for this book is available from the British
Library.

Published by Destinworld Publishing Ltd.
www.destinworld.com

Printed and bound in Great Britain by Marston Book Services Ltd, Oxfordshire

Contents

Introduction

Welcome to the first edition of Preserved Airliners and Transports of Europe, the only listing currently available covering aircraft designed for transporting people and goods, be it for civilian or military purposes.

We have endeavoured to provide a comprehensive and up-to-date listing wherever possible, providing all of the information you need to be able to track down and see/log/photograph the aircraft listed in this guide. In many cases, research has involved the authors spending hours tracking down the current status of an airframe which in other places was listed as present or at a particular address when it has in fact moved on or been scrapped. We hope the result is useful to you, and an accurate account of the state of the aircraft.

The editor would welcome and updates on the contents of this book which can be corrected for future editions, for the good of all readers. Your eyes and ears on the ground are invaluable!

We sincerely hope you enjoy using this book and find its contents useful. Remember that many of the aircraft listed are part of museum collections, located on military installations, or even used as private homes. Therefore, we encourage you to take care and show respect, fully obtaining permission before venturing out to find them.

The Scope of Aircraft Listed

This book covers aircraft in the countries of Europe, including the Canary Islands, Iceland and the western part of Russia.

Pure civilian fans may not appreciate military content included in this guide, but the authors made a conscious decision to include every type of aircraft that could be classed as a transport, whether it has been in use for military operators or not. Therefore, we have included a good mix of aircraft types.

The definition of 'Preserved' in our eyes includes any aircraft which is being maintained for ongoing enjoyment or work, including all museum pieces, gate guardians, private homes, and instructional aircraft such as those found in use with technical colleges and fire training departments.

We have also included aircraft which are not in one piece, whether awaiting reassembly or simply reduced to a cockpit or fuselage section for display. Unless otherwise stated, all aircraft can be considered complete airframes (or thereabouts).

Where possible we have listed the current colours and markings work (even if inaccurate to the aircraft's history), its official serial, and the type of aircraft.

With the location information, we have included the street address to the aircraft or owner (in the case of museums), along with a web address where possible for further research into opening times and contact details.

Updates

Please forward any updates, corrections and missing aircraft for future editions to:

info@destinworld.com

Armenia

Ashtarak

Linch St, Ashtarak, Armenia

EK-88256	Yakovlev Yak-40	Armenian Air Lines Used as a restaurant.

Lake Sevan

Noyland Resort

Gegharkunik Marz, Chkalovka village, M10, 1514, Armenia

EK-88167	Yakovlev Yak-40	Armenian Air Lines On shore of Lake Sevan, off M10 road south of Lchasen.

Austria

Bad Vöslau

Austrian Aviation Museum
Flugfeldstraße, A-2540 Flugplatz Bad Vöslau
www.austrian-aviation-museum.com

G-AGRW	Vickers Viking 1A	Wears false Austrian Airlines colours.

Graz

Austrian Air Museum
Thalerhofstraße 52, 8073 Feldkirchen bei Graz, Austria
www.luftfahrtmuseum.at

2919	Antonov An-2	Poland Air Force
5094	VFW Transall C-160D	German Air Force
OE-LSA	Swearingen SA226TC Metro II	Fuselage

Heidenreichstein

Industriestraße 8, 3860 Heidenreichstein, Austria

OK-GBH	Ilyushin IL-62	Used as bar/restaurant

Kössen

Fliegerbar
Österreich, Thurnbichl 40, 6345 Kössen, Austria

9A-BAA	Antonov An-2TP	Fly Kössen Outside bar.

Salzburg

Salzburg Airport
Innsbrucker Bundesstraße 95, 5020 Salzburg, Austria

N86U	Douglas C-47A	First Austrian DC-3 Dakota Club. Marked OE-LBC. Wears Austrian Airlines colours. Airworthy.

Vienna

Technisches Museum fur Industrie
Mariahilfer Str. 212, 1140 Wien, Austria
www.technischesmuseum.at

OE-BVM	De Havilland DH.104 Dove	Austrian Airlines

Zeltweg

Austrian Military Exhibition
Zeltweg Air Force Base
Flughafen, Flatschacher Str., 8740 Zeltweg, Austria

5S-TA	Short SC-7 Skyvan	Austrian Air Force

Belarus

Biahoml/Begoml

Roundabout on M3/P3 Crossroad

02 Red	Ilyusin IL-14T	Soviet Air Force

Chachersk

Ulitsa Lenina, beside Town Hall

53 Red	Tupolev Tu-124Sch	Soviet Air Force

Gomel

Gomel Airport

EW-46835	Antonov An-24	Gomelavia Instructional airframe

Korobchitsy

Woodland area, south west of town

03 Yellow	Antonov An-26	Belarus Air Force

Minsk

Belarus Aerospace Museum
Borovaya Airfield
aircraft-museum.ucoz.ru

04 Yellow	Antonov An-2B	Belarus Air Force
EK-11986	Antonov An-12TB	Fake Soviet Air Force markings
01 Yellow	Antonov An-24B	Belarus Air Force
22 Yellow	Antonov An-26	Belarus Air Force
CCCP-41865	Ilyushin IL-14P	Aeroflot
CCCP-75781	Ilyushin IL-18V	Aeroflot
RA-65038	Tupolev Tu-134A	Fake Aeroflot markings
EW-88187	Yakovlev Yak-40	Government of Belarus
RA-87414	Yakovlev Yak-40	Aeroflot Marked CCCP-87855

Chyzhowka Technical School

EW-70383	Antonov An-2	Instructional airframe
EW-46607	Antonov An-24RV	Aeroflot Instructional airframe
EW-65614	Tupolev Tu-134	Aeroflot Instructional airframe
EW-65663	Tupolev Tu-134A	Aeroflot Instructional airframe
EW-85122	Tupolev Tu-154B	Aeroflot Instructional airframe
EW-87775	Yakovlev Yak-40	Aeroflot Instructional airframe

Great Patriotic War Museum
Prospekt Pobediteley 8, Minsk, Belarus
www.warmuseum.by

56 Blue	Lisunov Li-2	Soviet Air Force

Machulishchi Airfield
Ulitsa Gvardeyskaya 13, Machulishchy, Belarus

24 Yellow	Antonov An-26 RTR	Belarus Air Force Marked '50 Red'

Minsk International Airport
Outside Terminal

EW-237CD	Antonov An-2R	GrodnoAvia
EW-47291	Antonov An-24RV	Gomelavia
EW-76709	Ilyushin IL-76 T	TransAVIAexport
EW-85581	Tupolev Tu-154 B2	Belavia
EW-88202	Yakovlev Yak-40	Minskavia

Mogilev

Gorodskoy Park
Pushkin Avenue, Mahilioŭ, Belarus

CCCP-65609	Tupolev Tu-134	Aeroflot

MOI Higher College
Krupskaj St 67, Mogilev 212011, Belarus

EW-87658	Yakovlev Yak-40	Mogileavia

Novo Pashkovo Airfield

EW-045AB	Antonov An-2T	

Svetlaya Roshcha

MChS (Training centre)

SP-FPL	Antonov An-26	Ex-Belavia Instructional airframe
Unknown	Tupolev Tu-134A	Ex-Belavia Instructional airframe

Zaslavl

Stalin Line Museum
Р28, 31 км, Лошанский с/с 223038, Belarus

03 White	Antonov An-2	Belarus Air Force

Belgium

Brussels

Melsbroek Air Base
1820 Steenokkerzeel, Belgium

LX-DKT	Douglas C-47A	Belgian Air Force Marked OT-CWA
CP-10	Fairchild C-119G Boxcar	Belgian Air Force
RM-7	Percival C.51 Pembroke	Belgian Air Force Marked OT-ZAG

Royal Museum of the Armed Forces and Military History
Parc du Cinquantenaire, 1000 Brussel, Belgium
www.klm-mra.be

OO-SJA	Boeing 707-329	SABENA Cockpit
B-06	Britten Norman A-21 Defender	Belgian Air Force
OO-SUD	De Havilland Canada DHC-3 Otter	Belgian Air Force
K-16	Douglas C-47B	Belgian Air Force
CP-46	Fairchild C-119G Boxcar	Belgian Air Force
OO-AGU	Junkers Ju52	Junkers
RM-4	Percival C.51 Pembroke	Belgian Air Force
OO-SRA	Sud SE.210 Caravelle 6N	SABENA

Charleroi

Rue Devillez 79, 6060 Charleroi, Belgium

5N-AUG	Airbus A310-329	Used as a café/restaurant

Ostend

Ostend Airport

5N-VRG	Boeing 707-355C	Part of fuselage used as a store at Oostend Air College.
EC-IDQ	Boeing 727-223F	Ground trainer

St Ghislain

St Ghislain Airport
Rue de la Rivièrette 53, 7330 Saint-Ghislain, Belgium

5X-JOE	McDonnell Douglas DC-10-30CF	Cockpit. Inside hangar. ex-DAS Air Cargo

Waarschoot

Kokorico Nightclub
Grote Baan 22, 9930 Zomergem, Belgium
www.kokorico.be

G-AZNA	Vickers Viscount 813	Mounted on poles

Wetteren

Expo Gowalt

Kwatrechtsteenweg 114, 9230 Wetteren, Belgium
www.expogowalt.be

TY-BBW	Boeing 707-321	Government of Benin. Fuselage and wings mounted on roof.

Bulgaria

Bourgas

Aviation Expo Museum (Closed)
Bourgas Airport
Future of exhibits uncertain.

LZ-1089	Antonov An-2R	
LZ-BAB	Antonov An-12B	
LZ-7001	Antonov An-14	Bulgarian Government
LZ-AND	Antonov An-24B	Balkan Bulgarian Nose section
LZ-ANF	Antonov An-24B	Balkan Bulgarian Nose section
LZ-ANL	Antonov An-24B	Balkan Bulgarian
LZ-BTJ	Tupolev Tu-154 B2	Balkan Bulgarian

Bourgas Airport

LZ-ILE	Ilyushin Il-14P	Balkan Bulgarian. Parked on roundabout near terminal.

Dobrosclavci

Dobrosclavci Air Base

095	Ilyushin Il-14	Bulgarian Air Force

Ihitman

Air Sofia Golf Club
1, Shesti Septemvri, ulitsa "Sveti Patriarh Evtimij", 2050 Ihtiman, Bulgaria

LZ-TUF	Tupolev Tu-134	Fuselage part of club house

Plovdiv

Aviation Museum
Plovdiv Airport, 4112, Bulgaria
www.airmuseum-bg.com

025	Antonov An-2M	Bulgarian Air Force
110	Antonov An-14	Bulgarian Air Force
LZ-ANE	Antonov An-24B	Balkan Bulgarian
097	Ilyushin Il-14	Bulgarian Air Force
062	LET 410 UVP	Bulgarian Air Force
CCCP-13381	Lisunov Li-2	
LZ-DOS	Yakovlev Yak-40	Hemus Air Under restoration

Razgrad

Anti-Terrorist Training Centre

LZ-TUC	Tupolev Tu-134	Ex-Balkan Bulgarian

Silistra

Play Park
ul. "Kapitan Krastev", 7504 Silistra

LZ-TUO	Tupolev Tu-134	Balkan Bulgarian

Sofia

Sofia Airport

LZ-TUZ	Tupolev Tu-134 A-3	Ex-Balkan Bulgarian. Instructional trainer north of runway.

Sunny Beach

Karting Sunny Beach
България, 9, Burgas, Bulgaria

LZ-914	Antonov An-2	

Varna

Varna Bay, Black Sea

LZ-BTJ	Tupolev Tu-154 B-1	Underwater. Diving attraction.

Croatia

Osijek

Osijek Airport
Vukovarska ul. 67, 31207, Klisa, Croatia

9A-BHV	Antonov An-2R	Aeroclub Osijek

Otocac

Otocac Airfield

71255	Douglas C-47A	Yugoslav Air Force

Rijeka

Rijeka Airport

9A-CBG	McDonnell Douglas MD-82	Forward fuselage Ground trainer

Vukovar

Memorial Centre of Homeland War
bb,, Ul. Ive Tijardovića, 32000, Vukovar, Croatia
www.mcdrvu.hr

9A-BHT	Antonov An-2R

Zadar

Zadar Airport Airbase

71203	Douglas C-47A	Yugoslav Air Force
		Poor condition

Czech Republic

Bakov

Fast Food Plane
Na Návsi 705, 294 01 Bakov nad Jizerou, Czechia

OK-WAJ	Ilyushin IL-18 D	Used as cafe

Bubovice

Bubovice Airfield
Bubovická 4, 267 18 Bubovice, Czechia

3109	Ilyushin/Avia-14 T	Czechoslovak Air Force

Chvalovice

Excalibur City Jet Rest
Chvalovice, 66902 Chvalovice-Hatě, 669 02 Chvalovice, Czechia
www.excaliburcity.com

OK-FBF	Ilyushin IL-62	Used as a restaurant

Holešov

Police Training Centre
Osvobozeni, 769 01 Holešov

0730	LET 410 UVP	Instructional airframe

Konesin

Letecke Museum
Koněšín Areál radarka Koněšín, 675 00 Koněšín, Czechia#
www.letecke-muzeum.cz

OK-WLT	Corvus F1	
0603	Ilyushin IL-14 FG	Czechoslovak Air Force

Kunovice

Letecke Museum
Letecká 1383, 686 04 Kunovice, Czechia
www.museum-kunovice.cz

3157	Ilyushin/Avia-14 P	Czechoslovak Air Force
1103	Ilyushin/Avia-14 FG	Czechoslovak Air Force
OK-022	LET 410 M	
OK-ADO	LET 410 A	
OK-ADP	LET 410 A	
0005	LET 610	Czech Air Force
1016	Tupolev Tu-154M	Czech Government Wings detached but present.

Lelekovice

U Vápenice, 664 31 Lelekovice

OK-KIE	Antonov An-2R	In Private Garden

Louny

SEKO Aerospace Factory
5. května 2940, 440 01 Louny, Czechia

OK-020	Yakovlev Yak-40	SEKO Airlines Marked OK-TSE

Petrovice

Air Restaurant
Petrovice 108, 403 37 Ústí nad Labem, Czechia
www.airrestaurant.cz

OK-LDC	Tupolev Tu-104A	Used as a restaurant

Prague

Army Museum
Kbely Airfield
Mladoboleslavská 425/9, 197 00 Kbely, Czechia
www.vhu.cz

2904	Antonov An-24B	Czech Air Force
7109	Antonov An-24B	Czech Air Force
2507	Antonov An-26	Czech Air Force

N143J	Douglas DC-3	CSA Czechoslovak Airlines Marked OK-XDM
3108	Ilyushin/Avia-14 T	Czechoslovak Air Force
3002	Lisunov Li-2	Czechoslovak Air Force
1504	LET 410 UVP	Czech Air Force
OK-LDA	Tupolev Tu-104A	CSA Czechoslovak Airlines
OK-BYG	Yakovlev Yak-40	Czech Government

Letiste Tocna Airfield
143 01 Prague 12, Czechia
www.tocna.cz

LZ-913	Antonov An-2	

Staré Město

Kovosteel Factory
Brněnská 1372, 686 03 Staré Město, Czechia

OK-130	LET 610	Kovosteel Mounted on poles outside factory.

Vyskov

Museum of Air and Ground Techniques
Letiště Vyškov, 682 01 Vyškov, Czechia
www.lhs-vyskov.cz

3133	Ilyushin/Avia-14	Czechoslovak Air Force
3144	Ilyushin/Avia-14 T	Czechoslovak Air Force

Zruc-Senev

Air Park
180, 330 08 Zruč–Senec, Czechia
www.airpark.wz.cz

7110	Antonov An-24B	Czech Air Force Wings from different aircraft
1107	Antonov An-30	Czech Air Force Open Skies markings
N49548	Boeing KC-97G	Rear fuselage and tail
6103	Ilyushin/Avia-14 M	Czechoslovak Air Force
3145	Ilyushin/Avia-14T	Czechoslovak Air Force Marked OK-LCC
3146	Ilyushin/Avia-14	Czechoslovak Air Force
0507	Ilyushin IL-14	Czechoslovak Air Force
OK-PAE	Ilyushin IL-18V	CSA Czechoslovak Airlines
OK-EKB	LET 410 A	
OK-028	LET 410 UVP	
OK-IYB	LET 410 UVP	
OK-NDF	Tupolev Tu-104A	CSA Czechoslovak Airlines
OK-DFI	Tupolev TU-134A	CSA Czechoslovak Airlines
1003	Tupolev Tu-154M	Czech Government

Denmark

Copenhagen

Technical Education Copenhagen
Stamholmen 193-215, 2650 Hvidovre, Denmark
www.tec.dk

N10EA	Jet Commander 1121	Instructional airframe

Helsingør

Fabriksvej 25, 3000 Helsingør, Denmark
www.tekniskmuseum.dk

NR676	De Havilland DH.89 Dragon Rapide	Marked OY-AAO
K-681	Douglas C-47A	Royal Danish Air Force Marked OY-DDA
OY-KNB	Douglas DC-7C	Conair. Forward fuselage.
OY-KRD	Sud SE.210 Caravelle 3	SAS Scandinavian Airlines

Karup

Danish Air Force Historic Collection
Herningvej 30, 7470 Viborg, Denmark
www.karupflymuseum.dk

OY-AVA	Percival President 1	Danish Air Force. Under restoration.

Roskilde

Roskilde Airport

| OY-BPB | Douglas C-47A | Association for Flying Museum Planes. Marked K-682. Airworthy. |

Skanderborg

Alongisde E45 motorway, exit 51
www.727.dk

| G-BNNI | Boeing 727-276 | Ex-Sabre Airways |

Slagelse

Panzermuseum East

Fladholtevej 18, 4200 Slagelse, Denmark
www.panzermuseumeast.dk

| G-AVMN | BAC 1-11-50ED | Painted in army colours |

Stauning

Danmarks Flymuseum

Lufthavnsvej 1, 6900 Skjern, Denmark
www.flymuseum.dk

| OY-SBR | Aerospatiale SN.601 Corvette | |
| WB534 / OY-BHZ | De Havilland DH.104 Dove | Dansk Faldskaerms Union. Parked away from museum. |

Denmark

OY-DHZ	De Havilland DH.104 Dove	Cimber Air
K-687	Douglas C-47A	Royal Danish Air Force
OY-ASY	Embraer 110 Bandeirante	Under restoration. ETA 2020
L-861	PBY-6A Catalina	Royal Danish Air Force

Estonia

Keila

Keila Model Flying Club
Keila, 76616 Harju County, Estonia

82 Red	Antonov An-12BP	ex Soviet Air Force Used by Keila Model Flying Club

Lange

Estonian Aircraft Museum
Lange, 62115 Tartu County, Estonia
www.lennundusmuuseum.ee

YL-LEB	Antonov An-2	Latavio
ES-LTA	Tupolev Tu-134A-3	ELK Airways
UR-87590	Yakovlev Yak-40	UES-Avia

Tallinn

Tallinn Airport
Suur-Sõjamäe 56a, 11415 Tallinn, Estonia

ES-AAP	Tupolev Tu-134A-3	Ground trainer parked at eastern end of airport, alongside 290/Suur-Sõjamäe.

Finland

PowerPark Amusement Centre
Puistotie 3, 62300 Kauhava, Finland
www.powerpark.fi

RA-46576	Antonov An-24	Mounted on concrete plinths.

Finnish Aviation Museum
Karhumäentie 12, 01530 Vantaa, Finland
www.ilmailumuseo.fi

OH-LRB	Convair CV-440	Finnair Rebuilt from CV-340
OH-VKB	Douglas DC-3A	Kar-Air
OH-LCD	Douglas DC-3	Finnish Airlines
D-BAKG	Fokker F27-200	Cockpit
OH-VKU	Lockheed Lodestar 18-56	Kar-Air
54-0160	Lockheed NC-121C Super Constellation	Cockpit

Kuovola

Service Station
Lentoportintie 3, 45410 Kouvola, Finland

RA-70623	Antonov An-2	

Pori

Pori Airport Technical College
Tallitie 14, 28540 Pori, Finland

FF-2	Fokker F27-100	Finnish Air Force. Ground trainer.
FF-3	Fokker F27-400M	Finnish Air Force. Ground trainer.

Rovaniemi

Rovaniemi Technical Vocational School

OH-GLB	Learjet 24D	Instructional airframe

Tampere

Tampere Airport

N569D	Dassault Falcon 20F	Instructional airframe

Tikkakoski

Aviation Museum of Central Finland
Tikkakoskentie 125, 41160 Tikkakoski, Finland
www.ilmavoimamuseo.fi

DO-4	Douglas C-47B	Finnish Air Force
PR-2	Percival Pembroke C53	Finnish Air Force. Stored in pieces.

Tuulos

Tuulonen Shopping Centre
Tuulosentie 1, 14810 Tuulos, Finland
www.tuulonen.fi

DO-1	Douglas DC-2	Finnish Air Force

Utti

Utti Airport

DO-5	Douglas C-47A	Finnish Air Force. Fuselage. Ground trainer.

France

L'Epopee de l'Industrie et de l'Aeronautique
17 Rue de l'Industrie, 80300 Albert, France
www.musee-eia.com

F-BPJR	Boeing 727-228	Air Charter Forward fuselage
F-GEOA	Douglas C-47	Marked 2108979
54	Nord Noratlas	French Air Force
97	Nord Noratlas	French Air Force
125	Nord Noratlas	French Air Force Fuselage
184	Nord Noratlas	French Air Force
189	Nord Noratlas	French Air Force
F-BHRY	Sud SE.210 Caravelle 3	Air France
148	Dassault Flamant	French Air Force
275	Dassault Flamant	French Air Force
F-BTTG	Dassault Mercure 100	Air Inter Forward fuselage

Allibaudieres

F-GDAE	Learjet 24	Mounted on pole next to road at southern end of village.

Avignon

Avignon Airport
141 Allée de la Chartreuse, 84140 Avignon, France

F-BOHA	Sud SE.210 Caravelle 3	Air France. Parked near terminal entrance.

Avord

Avord Air Base

146	Dassault Flamant	French Air Force
229	Dassault Flamant	French Air Force
073	Embraer Xingu	French Air Force

Barcelonnette

Aérodrome de Saint-Pons
04400 Barcelonette, France

200	Dassault Flamant	French Air Force

Beauvais

Musee de Warluis
Rue des Bruyères, 60430 Warluis, France
www.museedelaviation-warluis.com

HB122	Beech C18S	French Air Force

Bordeaux

Conservatoire de L'Air et L'Espace D'Aquitane

Avenue de l'Argonne, 33700 Mérignac, France
www.caea.info

F-WMSH	Dassault Falcon 20	
F-WAMD	Dassault Falcon 30	Fuselage
F-WNDB	Dassault Falcon 50	Fuselage
202	Dassault Flamant	French Air Force
F-BTTF	Dassault Mercure 100	Air Inter North side of airport. Poor condition.
188	Nord Noratlas	French Air Force
282	Nord NC.702 Martinet	French Air Force
234/F-ZACQ	Sud SE.210 Caravelle 6R	French Air Force 'Zero G'. North side of airport. Poor condition.

Bregny

Ecole Catholique d'Apprentissage de l'Automobile E.C.A.U.T

301 Route de Bregny, 74250 Viuz-en-Sallaz, France
www.ecaut.com

146	Nord Noratlas	French Air Force

Bretigny-sur-Orge

Bretigny Air Base

342	Dassault Falcon 20	Instructional airframe

Cannes

Mandelieu Airport
245 Avenue Francis Tonner, 06150 Cannes, France

F-BUOP	Beech 18	Marked F-BCCI. At airport entrance.

Carentan

101st Airborne Division Memorial
7B Boulevard de Verdun, 50500 Carentan, France

N3455	Douglas C-47	Fuselage

Castelnau-Magnoc

Castelnau-Magnoc Aerodrome
65230 Castelnau-Magnoac

220	Dassault Flamant	French Air Force

Châteaudun

Conservatory CANOPEE Châteaudun
Route d'Orléans, 28200 Châteaudun, France

790	De Havilland Canada DHC-6 Twin Otter	French Air Force
182	Dassault Falcon 20	French Air Force
191	Dassault Flamant	French Air Force
89	Nord 262	French Air Force
171	Nord Noratlas	French Air Force

Creil

Creil Aeroclub
2 Avenue de la Forêt d'Halatte, 60100 Creil, France

F-BICV	Hurel-Dubois HD-34	Poor condition

Evreux

Evreux Air Base

501	Breguet Deux Ponts	French Air Force
156	Nord Noratlas	French Air Force

Fontenay-Tresigny

Chaubuisson Airfield
Route de l'aérodrome de Chaubuisson, 77610 Fontenay-Trésigny, France

6	Breguet Deux Ponts	French Air Force Marked F-BACC

Frejus

Frejus Airfield (Closed)

113	Dassault Flamant	French Air Force

France

Gourlizon

Le Moulin Nightclub
La Croix Neuve, 29100 Le Juch, France

| F-BHBG | Lockheed L-1049G Constellation | Super G titles. |

La Ferte Alais

Amicale Jean-Baptiste Salis
Aérodrome de Cerny-la Ferté-Alais, 91590 Cerny / La-Ferté-Alais, France
www.ajbs.fr

F-AZEJ	Beech E18S	Marked 436904
F-AZJU	CASA 352L	Airworthy
F-AZCA	De Havilland DH.89 Dragon Rapide	Airworthy
F-BHGR	De Havilland DH.89 Dragon Rapide	Air France. Airworthy.
F-AZTE	Douglas C-47	
F-BLOZ	Douglas C-47	Marked 313142
F-AZNH	Hurel-Dubois HD-34	
3	Nord 262	French Air Force

Lasclaveries

| 118 | Nord Noratlas | Used as a bar |

Latresne

Aero Campus Aquitaine
1 Route de Cénac, Aerocampus Aquitaine, 33360 Latresne, France

145	Dassault Falcon 20	French Air Force. Instructional airframe.

Les Mureaux

Airbus
51 78133 Cedex, 61 Route de Verneuil, 78130 Les Mureaux, France

202	Nord Noratlas	French Air Force. Parked outside factory.

Lorient

Lann-Bihoue Airport
Military Base, D765, 56530 Quéven, France

4	Beech 18	French Navy
87	Douglas C-47	French Navy

Lyon

Lyon Saint Exupery Airport

C-FTNA	Lockheed L1011 TriStar 150	Ex-Air Transat. Preserved south of terminals.

Musée de l'Aviation Clément Ader
370 Rue Nungesser et Coli, 69960 Corbas, France
www.ealc.fr

167	Dassault Falcon 20	French Air Force
60	Nord 262	French Navy

Martignas-sur-Jalle

Dassault Aviation
Avenue Martyrs de la Résistance, 33127 Martignas-sur-Jalle, France

F-WDFJ	Dassault Falcon 20	

Merville

Institute Aeronautics Amaury De La Grange
Rue du docteur Rousseau, Aérodrome de Merville-Calonne, 59660 Mervillle,
France
www.iaag-aero.com

F-BOJA	Boeing 727-228	Ex-Air France. Instructional airframe.
129	Nord Noratlas	French Air Force. Instructional airframe.
F-BHRT	Sud SE.210 Caravelle 3	Air France. Instructional airframe. Inside hangar.
F-GCVK	Sud SE.210 Caravelle 12	Air Inter. Instructional airframe.
F-BMCF	Vickers Viscount 724	Air Inter. Instructional airframe.

Musee de la batterie de Merville

Place du 9ème Bataillon, 14810 Merville-Franceville-Plage, France
www.batterie-merville.com

71248	Douglas C-47	US Air Force. Marked 315073.

Montelimar

Musee Europeen de l'Aviation de Chasse

Chemin de l'entrée de l'Aérodrome, 26200 Montélimar, France
www.meacmtl.com

86	Dassault Falcon 20	French Air Force
F-AZEO	Dassault Flamant	
172	Dassault Flamant	French Air Force
N56NA	Douglas DC-3	
EC-GGB	Douglas DC-7	Cockpit
116/F-ZACE	Sud SE.210 Caravelle 3	French Air Force

Montpellier

Montpellier Airport

F-GBEJ	Nord 262	Instructional airframe

Moyenpal

324-360 Chemin de Rasey, 88220 Xertigny, France

F-BYCY	Sud SE.210 Caravelle 6N	Used as a hotel

Nantes

Amicale du Super Constellation
de, Route de Fremiou, 44860 Saint-Aignan-Grandlieu, France
www.superconstellation-nantes.fr

F-BRAD	Lockheed L-1049G Constellation	Air France. Marked F-BGNJ.

Nantes Airport

18	Nord Noratlas	French Air Force. Poor condition.

Orleans
Orleans-Bricy Air Base
Rue de la Base, 45140 Boulay-les-Barres, France

29	Nord Noratlas	French Air Force
R155	VFW Transall C-160D	Cockpit

Pamiers

1st Parachute Regiment
Quartier Capitaine Beaumont, 09100 Pamiers, France

196	Nord Noratlas	French Air Force

Paris

Stade de la Rose des Vents
6 rue Louison Bobet, BP 135, 93623 Aulnay-sous-Bois, France

50	Nord Noratlas	French Air Force

Charles de Gaulle Airport

F-BVFF	Aerospatiale/BAC Concorde 101	Air France. Mounted on poles near Terminal 3.

Air and Space Museum

Aéroport de Paris-Le Bourget, 93350 Le Bourget, France
www.museeairespace.fr

F-BTSD	Aerospatiale/BAC Concorde 101	Air France
F-WTSS	Aerospatiale/BAC Concorde 001	Aerospatiale
F-WWDD	Airbus A380-861	Airbus
N61909	Beech 18	In storage
F-BLCD	Boeing 707-328B	Air France. In storage.
N166FE	Boeing 727-22F	FedEx Express. In storage.
F-BVPJ	Boeing 747-128	Air France
04	Breguet 941	French Air Force. In storage.
F-BMSS	Dassault Falcon 20	In storage
F-WLKB	Dassault Falcon 20	
130	Dassault Flamant	In storage
280	Dassault Flamant	In storage
F-BTTD	Dassault Mercure 100	Air Inter
F-BHCD	De Havilland DH.89 Dragon Rapide	
49194	Douglas C-47	US Air Force. Cockpit.
92449	Douglas C-47	French Air Force. Marked 42-100558
45016	Douglas DC-7	French Air Force. In storage.
45570	Douglas DC-8-53	French Air Force.

F-HMFU	Farman F.60 Goliath	Fuselage
1607	HFB-320 Hansajet	German Air Force
F-BICR	Hurel-Dubois HD-34	
Unknown	Junkers F13	
216	Junkers Ju52	French Air Force. In storage.
R18	VFW Transall C-160D	French Air Force
F-ZVMV	Lockheed L-649 Constellation	Air France. In storage.
01	Nord 260	French Air Force
16	Nord 262	In storage
72	Nord 262	In storage
162	Nord Noratlas	French Air Force. In storage.
194	Nord Noratlas	French Air Force. In storage.
F-BZCK	Nord Noratlas	French Air Force. In storage.
F-BNAN	Potez 842	In storage
F-OBIP	Short Sandringham	In storage
F-GJAP	Aerospatiale SN.601 Corvette	In storage
141/F-RAFG	Sud SE.210 Caravelle 3	French Air Force. In storage.
F-BHHI	Sud SE.210 Caravelle	Cockpit. Prototype.
F-GCVL	Sud SE.210 Caravelle 12	Air Provence

Musee Delta, Paris Orly

40 Avenue Jean-Pierre Bénard, 91200 Athis-Mons, France
www.museedelta.wixsite.com

F-WTSA	Aerospatiale/BAC Concorde 02

Orly Airport

SU-DAS	Airbus A300B4-203	Ground trainer
F-BVPZ	Sud SE.210 Caravelle 6N	Ground trainer

Pau

Parachute Museum
Cité des parachutistes, Chemin d'Astra, 64140 Lons, France
www.museedesparas.com

161	Nord Noratlas	French Air Force

Peyrehorade

Lycee Professionnel Regional Jean Taris
365 Avenue Jean Dupaya, 40300 Peyrehorade, France
www.lycee-jean-taris-40.net

186	Dassault Falcon 20	French Air Force. Instructional airframe.

Rennes

Rennes Airport

F-GCVJ	Sud SE.210 Caravelle 12	Air Inter. Poor condition.

Rochefort

Musee de l'Aeronautique Navale

Rond-Point Albert Bignon, 17300 Rochefort, France
www.anaman.fr

25	Beech 18	French Navy
709	Beech 18	French Navy
294	Dassault Flamant	French Air Force
716	Douglas DC-3	French Navy
43	Nord 262	French Navy
59	Nord 262	French Navy
925	Piper PA-31	French Navy

Rochefort Charente-Maritime Airport

196	Dassault Flamant	French Air Force
122	Nord Noratlas	French Air Force

Saint Nazaire

Airbus Factory

60 Rue Anatole France, 44550 Montoir-de-Bretagne, France

F-WUQN	Aerospatiale SN.601 Corvette	Marked F-BUQN
37	Sud-Ouest Bretagne	French Air Force

Sainte Mere Eglise

Airborne Museum
14 Rue Eisenhower, 50480 Sainte-Mère-Église, France
www.airborne-museum.org

25	Douglas C-47	Wears false US Air Force colours and marked 315159
N4332E	Douglas C-47	Wears false US Air Force colours and marked 315510

Saint-Yan

Saint-Yan Airport
Route de Marigny, 71600 Saint-Yan, France

55	Nord 262	Marked F-BPNS

Tarbes

35th Parachute Artillery Regiment
Place courte boule, 65000 Tarbes, France

111	Nord Noratlas	French Air Force

Toulouse

Aeroscopia Museum
1 Allée André Turcat, 31700 Blagnac, France
www.musee-aeroscopia.fr

F-BPPA	Aero Spacelines Super Guppy	Aero Spacelines

France

F–BVFC	Aerospatiale/BAC Concorde 101	Air France
F–WTSB	Aerospatiale/BAC Concorde 100	Aerospatiale
F–WUAB	Airbus A300B4–203	Airbus
F–WWMT	Airbus A400M	Airbus. Prototype.
02/F–ZACB	Dassault Falcon 20	French Air Force
F–GMTO	Fairchild Merlin IVA	
F–GKGA	Aerospatiale SN.601 Corvette	
F–BTOE	Sud SE.210 Caravelle 12	Air Inter

Ailes Anciennes Museum
4 Rue Roger Béteille, 31700 Blagnac, France
www.aatise.org

03	Breguet 941	French Air Force
504	Breguet Deux Ponts	French Air Force
227	Dassault Flamant	French Air Force
G–ALWC	Douglas C–47A	
191	Nord Noratlas	French Air Force
F–GFLJ	Nord Noratlas	French Air Force
F–GHMU	Sud SE.210 Caravelle 10B3	Air Toulouse International

Center Tests Aeronautical De Toulouse
47 Rue Saint-Jean, 31130 Balma, France

55-0018	Lockheed C–130A Hercules	US Air Force. Fuselage. Instructional airframe.
F50	VFW Transall C–160D	French Air Force. Fuselage. Instructional airframe.
208	Nord Noratlas	French Air Force

48

Francazal Airport

115	Nord Noratlas	French Air Force. Located on military side.

Tours

Tours Airport
rond point De L'Aviation, 37210 Parçay-Meslay, France

F-BTMA	Beech 99	TAT. On roundabout north of airport.

Toussus-le-Noble

Ecole Technique Air France
78117 Toussus-le-Noble Aerodrome, France

124	Dassault Falcon 20	Instructional airframe
238/F-RAEE	Dassault Falcon 20	Instructional airframe

Vannes

Morbihan Aéro Musée
Ker Haliguen, 56250 Monterblanc, France
www.morbihan-aero-musee.com

160	Nord Noratlas	

Villeneuve-sur-Lot

Villeneuve-sur-Lot Aerodrome
D661, 47300 Villeneuve-sur-Lot, France

F-AZEH	Dassault Flamant	

Visan-Valreas

Visan-Valreas Aerodrome
84820 Visan

253	Dassault Flamant	French Air Force

Vitrolles

Technic School Pierre Mendes
Avenue Yitzhak Rabin, 13127 Vitrolles, France
www.ac-aix-marseille.fr

2	Aerospatiale SN.601 Corvette	French Air Force. Instructional airframe.
F-BUQP	Aerospatiale SN.601 Corvette	Instructional airframe

Germany

Flugwelt- und Luftfahrtmuseum

Flugpl. 5, 04603 Nobitz, Germany
www.flugwelt-altenburg-nobitz.de

61+12	Breguet 1150 Atlantic	German Air Force
5102	VFW Transall C-160D	German Air Force

Luftlande und Lufttransport Schule

Altenstadt Airfield, 86972 Altenstadt, Germany

5003	VFW Transall C-160D	Fuselage. Instructional airframe.
5337	Nord Noratlas	German Air Force

Otto Lilienthal Museum

Ellbogenstraße 1, 17389 Anklam, Germany
www.lilienthal-museum.de

D-FONG	Antonov An-2	Interflug. Marked DDR-DKG

Ankum

Museum für Technik, Natur und Luftfahrt
Am Kreuzplatz 4, 49577 Ankum

5037	VFW Transall C-160D	German Air Force

Bad Aibling

Pullacher Au 3, 83059 Kolbermoor, Germany

OK-JIM	Antonov An-2	Parked outside farmhouse

Bad Laer

Sanicare
Grüner Weg 1, 49196 Bad Laer, Germany

D-ABAH	Douglas DC-6	Sanicare

Bad Oeynhausen

Motortechnika Museum (closed)
Weserstraße 225, 32547 Bad Oeynhausen, Germany

SP-WWF	Antonov An-2	Future of aircraft uncertain

Ballenstedt

Ballenstedt Airfield
Rathausplatz 12, 06493 Ballenstedt, Germany

5007	VFW Transall C-160D	German Air Force. For Luftfahrtmuseum Wernigerode?

Bensheim

Auerbach Museum
Schillerstraße, 64625 Bensheim, Germany

0402	LET 410	Czech Air Force

Berlin

Allied Museum
Clayallee 135, 14195 Berlin, Germany
www.alliiertenmuseum.de

TG503	Handley Page Hastings	Royal Air Force

German Museum of Technology
Trebbiner Str. 9, 10963 Berlin, Germany
www.sdtb.de

N951CA	Douglas DC-3	Marked 45-951
D-AZAW	Junkers Ju52	Real identity unknown

Military History Museum Berlin-Gatow

Am Flugplatz Gatow 33, 14089 Berlin, Germany
www.mhm-gatow.de

822	Antonov An-2	East German Air Force
995	Antonov An-14	East German Air Force
5209	Antonov An-26	German Air Force
1626	HFB 320 Hansa Jet	German Air Force
5310	LET 410	German Air Force
5056	VFW Transall C-160D	German Air Force
9914	Nord Noratlas	German Air Force
5407	Percival Pembroke	German Air Force. Marked XA-107.
ZD215	Douglas C-47	Royal Air Force. Marked A65-69.

Tegel Airport

N130KR	Boeing 707-458	False Lufthansa scheme. Marked D-ABOC. Poor condition at west end of airport.

Tempelhof Airport (Closed)

12101 Berlin, Germany

58-02020	De Havilland Canada DHC-2 Beaver	US Army
45-0557	Douglas C-54	US Air Force
D-CARE	HFB 320 Hansa Jet	Parked in centre of airfield. To be restored.
N614GB	VFW-Fokker 614	

Biberach

HYDRO Systems
Ahfeldstraße 10, 77781 Biberach, Germany

| DDR-SCL | Tupolev Tu-134A | |

Borkheide

Hans-Grade Museum
Am Flugplatz, 14822 Borkheide, Germany
www.l-fischer.de

| DDR-STE | Ilyushin IL-18 | Interflug |

Bremen

Bremen Airport

| D-IOSA | Piper PA-42 Cheyenne | Lufthansa
Parked outside Lufthansa Flight Training near terminal. |
| D-ASAX | VFW-Fokker 614 | Mounted on terminal roof.
Marked D-BABK. |

Cammerswalde

Gaststätte am Flugzeug
Hauptstraße 104, 09544 Neuhausen/Erzgebirge, Germany

| DM-SAB | Ilyushin IL-14 | Interflug.
Parked outside restaurant. |

Cologne

Cologne/Bonn Airport
Flughafen Köln/Bonn, 51147 Köln, Germany

F-BUAD	Airbus A300B2-103C	Zero-G. Preserved near terminal.
D-AELM	Fokker F27-600(F)	Under restoration. To be displayed.

Cottbus

Flugplatzmuseum Cottbus
Fichtestraße 1, 03046 Cottbus, Germany
www.flugplatzmuseumcottbus.de

826	Antonov An-2	East German Air Force
996	Antonov An-14	East German Air Force

Dessau

Technikmuseum Hugo Junkers
Kühnauer Str. 161a, 06846 Dessau, Germany
www.technikmuseum-dessau.de

DM-SAF	Ilyushin IL-14	Wears false Lufthansa colours
1ZBY	Junkers Ju52	German Air Force

Dresden

Dresden Airport
Grenzstraße 1, 01109 Dresden, Germany

DM-SAL	Ilyushin IL-14	Wears false Lufthansa colours. Preserved outside EADS facility.

Eitorf

Maschinenbau Feld GmbH – Laserzuschnitte & Blechbearbeitung
Im Auel 34, 53783 Eitorf, Germany

CCCP-7348	Antonov An-2	Aeroflot

Erfurt

Erfurt Airport

DDR-STG	Ilyushin IL-18	Ex-Interflug. Instructional airframe, parked on main apron.

Finow

Luftfahrt Museum Finowfurt
Museumsstraße 1, 16244 Schorfheide, Germany
www.luftfahrtmuseum-finowfurt.de

DM-SKO	Antonov An-2	Interflug
482	Ilyushin IL-14	East German Air Force

| DDR-SCH | Tupolev Tu-134 | Interflug |

Frankfurt

Frankfurt/Main Airport

D-ABJI	Boeing 737-530	Lufthansa. Instructional airframe.
D-AMAJ	British Aerospace BAe 146-200	Ex-WDL. Marked D-NICE. Instructional airframe.
N1350M	Douglas C-47	US Air Force. Marked 349081. Berlin Airlift Memorial.
N88887	Douglas C-54	US Air Force. Marked 9063. Berlin Airlift Memorial.

Friedrichshafen

Dornier Museum

Claude-Dornier-Platz 1, 88046 Friedrichshafen, Germany
www.dorniermuseum.de

D-CICE	Dornier 228	DLR
D-ICDO	Dornier 228	DLR
D-BEJR	Dornier 328-300	Dornier

Grossenhain

Fliegendes Museum
Zum Fliegerhorst 13, 01558 Großenhain, Germany

D-FOFM	Antonov An-2	
D-ILIT	De Havilland DH.89 Dragon Rapide	Airworthy

Grunz

Private Home
Dorfstraße 15, 17328 Penkun, Germany

CCCP-65745	Tupolev Tu-134	

Hamburg

Finkenwerder Airport

F-GDSG	Aero Spacelines Super Guppy	Airbus
D-CARA	HFB 320 Hansa Jet	
5062	VFW Transall C-160D	German Air Force
157	Nord Noratlas	French Air Force

Hamburg Airport

D-ABOD	Boeing 707-430	Lufthansa. Marked D-ABOB. Parked north of terminal, airside.
D-ABIA	Boeing 737-530	Lufthansa. Instructional airframe.

Hanover

Luftfahrt Museum Hannover
Ulmer Str. 2, 30880 Laatzen, Germany
www.lufthfahrtmuseum-hannover.de

HA-MHM	Antonov An-2
D-CARY	HFB 320 Hansa Jet

Silbervogel Restaurant
Mercedesstraße 1, 30453 Hannover, Germany
www.restaurant-silbervogel.de

D-ANAB	Vickers Viscount 814	Used as café/restaurant

Hermeskeil

Hermeskeil Museum Flugausstellung P. Junior
B327, 54411 Hermeskeil, Germany
www.flugausstellung.de

HA-ANA	Antonov An-2	
5208	Antonov An-26	German Air Force
D-CIAD	CASA 352L	
T.2B-127	CASA 352L	
G-BDIW	De Havilland DH.106 Comet 4C	Dan-Air London
G-NAVY	De Havilland DH.104 Sea Devon	Royal Navy. Marked XJ348.
N62443	Douglas C-47	Wears false Royal Jordanian Air Force colours. Marked 111.
XX476	Handley Page Jetstream T2	Royal Navy
3076	Ilyushin IL-14	Polish Air Force

DDR-STH	Ilyushin IL-18	Interflug
D-ALIN	Lockheed L-1049G Super Constellation	Lufthansa
D-ACUT	Nord Noratlas	
5421	Percival Pembroke	German Air Force
5424	Percival Pembroke	Wears false Royal Air Force colours.
DDR-SCK	Tupolev Tu-134	Interflug
G-ARVF	Vickers VC10	UAE Government
D-ANAM	Vickers Viscount 814	Lufthansa

Hohn

Hohn Air Base

6320	Junkers Ju52	Wears false German Air Force colours.
5085	VFW Transall C-160D	German Air Force
5355	Nord Noratlas	German Air Force. Marked 5325.

Kamenz

Kamenz Airport
Zum Tower 6, 01917 Kamenz, Germany

D-FKMG	Antonov An-2	Marked 801

Koblenz

Wehrtechnische Studiensammlung
Mayener Str. 85, 56070 Koblenz, Germany
www.vffwts.de

199	Nord Noratlas	French Air Force

Landsberg

Penzing Air Base
Kauferinger Straße 1, 86929 Penzing, Germany

128	Nord Noratlas	French Air Force

Leipzig

Da Capo – Event Hall and Oldtimermuseum
Karl-Heine-Straße 105, 04229 Leipzig, Germany
www.michaelis-leipzig.de

DDR-STB	Ilyushin IL-18	Interflug. Mounted on building roof.

Restaurant Regenbogen
Arno-Nitzsche-Straße 43, 04277 Leipzig, Germany
www.regenbogenbowling.de

DDR-SEF	Ilyushin IL-62	Interflug. Used as café/restaurant.

Leverkusen

Esso Gas Station
Alkenrather Str. 69, 51377 Leverkusen, Germany

SP-WNU	Antonov An-2R	Mounted on poles.

Magdeburg

Restaurant PapaRazzi
Ottersleber Chaussee 99, 39120 Magdeburg, Germany
www.paparazzi-magdeburg.de

DDR-SCB	Tupolev Tu-134	Interflug

Manching

Ingolstadt Manchine Air Base
Zur General Aviation 2, 85077 Manching, Germany

LX-N20000	Boeing 707-307C	NATO. Instructional airframe.

Meresburg

Luftfahrt und Technik Museumspark Merseburg
Kastanienpromenade 50, 06217 Merseburg, Germany
www.luftfahrt-technik-museum.de

HA-MHL	Antonov An-2	
G-DEVN	De Havilland DH.104 Dove	
3065	Ilyushin IL-14	Polish Air Force
DDR-SEC	Ilyushin IL-62	Interflug

DDR-SCZ	Tupolev Tu-134	Interflug

Minden

Potts Park

Heinrich Pott GmbH & Co. KG, Bergkirchener Str. 99, 32429 Minden, Germany
www.pottspark-minden.de

D-ACUG	Nord Noratlas	

Mönchengladbach

Mönchengladbach Airport

D-AELL	Fokker F27-200(F)	Instructional airframe
EC-HRH	Cessna 500 Citation I	Instructional airframe

Munich

Deutsches Museum

Museuminsel 1, 80538 München, Germany
www.deutsches-museum.de

363	Junkers Ju52	French Air Force

Munich Airport Besucherpark

Nordallee 7, 85356 München-Flughafen, Germany

D-CIAS	CASA 352L	Marked D-ANOY
N65371	Douglas DC-3	Wears false Swissair colours. Marked IIB-IRN.
F-BHML	Lockheed L-1049G Constellation	Wears false Lufthansa colours. Marked D-ALEM.

Neuenkirchen

Interessenverein Luftfahrt Neuenkirchen
Warliner Str. 18, 17039 Neuenkirchen, Germany
www.ivln.de

D-FONB	Antonov An-2	Wears false East German Air Force colours. Marked 799.

Neideralteich

Gerhard Neumann Museum
10, Hengersberger Str. 8, 94557 Niederalteich, Germany
www.f-104.de

D-COSA	HFB 320 Hansa Jet

Nordholz

Aeronauticum Museum
Peter-Strasser-Platz 3, 27637 Wurster Nordseeküste, Germany
www.aeronauticum.de

61+06	Breguet 1150 Atlantic	German Navy
61+14	Breguet 1150 Atlantic	German Navy
59+19	Dornier 28 Skyservant	German Navy
5408	Percival Pembroke	German Air Force
D-AXDB	VFW-Fokker 614	German Air Force

Oberschleissheim

Deutsches Museum Flugwert Schleissheim
Effnerstraße 18, 85764 Oberschleißheim, Germany
www.deutsches-museum.de

03 Red	Antonov An-2	Soviet Air Force
1401	Douglas C-47D	German Air Force
D-CSPN	Grob 180	
D-CLOU	HFB 320 Hansa Jet	
D-ADAM	VFW-Fokker 614	DLR

Reichenbach

Autohaus Barnath
Kaltes Feld 1, 08468 Heinsdorfergrund, Germany

DM-ZZB	Ilyushin IL-14	Mounted on concrete blocks outside car garage.

Schwelm

Heidestraße 31, 58256 Ennepetal, Germany

5237	Nord Noratlas	Used as a bar?

Schwenningen

International Luftfahrt Museum
Spittelbronner Weg 78, 78056 Villingen-Schwenningen, Germany
www.luftfahrtmuseum.pflumm.eu

SP-AOG	Antonov An-2	

Seifertshofen

Swabian farmers and Technology Museum

Marktstraße 5, 73569 Eschach, Germany

www.museum-kiemele.de

5205	Antonov An-26	German Air Force
5343	Nord Noratlas	German Air Force
5417	Percival Pembroke	German Air Force

Sinsheim

Auto & Technik Museum

Eberhard-Layher-Straße 1, 74889 Sinsheim, Germany

sinsheim.technik-museum.de

F-BVFB	Aerospatiale/BAC Concorde 101	Air France Mounted on poles
HA-ANB	Antonov An-2	Marked '03 Red'
D-CIAL	CASA 352L	Marked D-2527. Mounted on poles.
N9012P	CASA 352L	Marked RJNP
D-IKER	De Havilland DH.104 Dove	Hung from ceiling.
N8041A	Douglas C-47	Wears false Lufthansa colours. Marked D-CADE. Mounted on poles.
0833	Ilyushin IL-14	Wears false Bulgarian Air Transport colours. Mounted on poles.
OK-PAI	Ilyushin IL-18	CSA Czechoslovak Airlines. Mounted on poles.
D-CAKE	Percival Pembroke	
HA-LBH	Tupolev Tu-134	Malev. Mounted on poles.

| CCCP-77112 | Tupolev Tu-144 | Aeroflot. Mounted on poles. |
| F-BGNU | Vickers Viscount 708 | Air Inter. Mounted on poles. |

Speyer

Technic Museum Speyer
Am Technik Museum 1, 67346 Speyer, Germany
speyer.technik-museum.de

RA-41343	Antonov An-2	Aeroflot
UR-64460	Antonov An-22	Antonov Airlines. Mounted on poles.
5204	Antonov An-26	Wears false East German Air Force colours
D-ABYM	Boeing 747-230	Lufthansa. Mounted on poles.
T.2B-209	CASA 352L	Wears false Lufthansa colours. Marked D-AQUI. Hung from ceiling.
F-BTTB	Dassault Mercuree 100	Air Inter. Mounted on poles.
F-BFGX	Douglas C-53	Air France. Mounted on poles.
VBUP	Junkers Ju52	German Air Force. Marked CAJY. Hung from ceiling.
5099	VFW Transall C-160D	German Air Force
154	Nord Noratlas	French Air Force. Mounted on poles.
D-ILUX	Rockwell Twin Commander 680F	Mounted on poles.
OY-TOR	VFW-Fokker 614	Cimber Air. Mounted on poles.
D-ANAF	Vickers Viscount 814	Lufthansa. Mounted on poles.

Stammheim

Maintalstraße, 97509 Kolitzheim, Germany
www.museum-stammheim.de

HA-MHQ	Antonov An-2	

Stölln-Rhinow

Otto Lilienthal Verein
Am Gollenberg 5, 14728 Gollenberg, Germany
www.otto-lilienthal.de

DDR-SEG	Ilyushin IL-62	Interflug

Stuttgart

Stuttgart Echterdingen Airport

SP-ANL	Antonov An-2T	Preserved on viewing terrace.

Twisteden

Irrland Theme Park
Am Scheidweg 1, 47624 Kevelaer, Germany
www.irrland.de

MM583	Aeritalia G222	Italian Air Force
RA-31516	Antonov An-2	
5098	VFW Transall C-160D	German Air Force

Wernigerode

Museum fur Luftfahrt und Technik
Gießerweg 1, 38855 Wernigerode, Germany
www.luftfahrtmuseum-wernigerode.de

HA-MER	Antonov An-2	
SP-WOS	Antonov An-2	Cockpit
EC-HBF	Fairchild Merlin IIIA	Cockpit

Wolgast

Autohaus Carsten Neumann
Am Fuchsberg 1, 17438 Wolgast, German

D-FONI	Antonov An-2	Mounted outside car showroom.

Wunstorf

Wunstorf Air Force Base Army Museum
Zur Luftbrücke 1, 31515 Wunstorf, Germany
www.ju52-halle.de

DBRD	Junkers Ju52	German Air Force
5107	VFW Transall C-160D	German Air Force
66	Nord Noratlas	Wears false German Air Force colours. Marked GR248.

Greece

Athens

BARIN Restaurant
33i 13, Elliniko 167 77, Greece

SX-ECD	Douglas C-47B	Used as bar/restaurant

Ellinikon Airport (Closed)
These airframes remain – for now.

SX-BAR	BAC 1-11-215AU	Hellenic Airlines
SX-CBA	Boeing 727-284	Olympic Airways
SX-BCA	Boeing 737-284	Olympic Airways
SX-OAB	Boeing 747-284B	Olympic Airways

Hellenic CAA Headquarters
Elliniko 167 77, Greece

SX-ECF	Douglas DC-3	Hellenic CAA

Elefsis

Elefsina Air Base Heritage Park
Ελευσίν, Leof. Gelas, Elefsina 192 00, Greece

92626	Douglas C-47B	Greek Air Force
510070	Grumman SHU-16B Albatross	Greek Air Force

517203	Grumman SHU-16B Albatross	Greek Air Force. Mounted on plinth.
2137	NAMC YS-11 A-220	Greek Air Force
52-128	Nord 2501D Noratlas	Greek Air Force

Katachas

Dc3 Cafe
Methoni 600 61, Greece

| 92641 | Douglas C-47B | Mounted on café roof |

Tanagra

Tanagra Air Base

| KK156 | Douglas C-47B | Greek Air Force |

Tatoi

Hellenic Air Force Museum
Dekelia Air Base, 13671, Tatoi
www.haf.gr

349111	Douglas C-47B	Greek Air Force
KJ960	Douglas C-47B	Greek Air Force
KK169	Douglas C-47B	Greek Air Force
P-9/120	Grumman G.159 Gulfstream 1	Greek Air Force
15289	Grumman SHU-16B Albatross	Greek Air Force
517190	Grumman SHU-16B Albatross	Greek Air Force
517204	Grumman SHU-16B Albatross	Greek Air Force

| D1+KG | Junkers Ju52 | Luftwaffe |
| 53-258 | Nord 2501D Noratlas | Greek Air Force |

Thessaloniki

Thessaloniki Airport

| HA-LCR | Tupolev Tu-154B-2 | Ex-Malev. Ground trainer. |

Thessaloniki Sedes Air Base Museum
Thermi 570 01, Greece

KN542	Douglas C-47B	Greek Air Force
KN575	Douglas C-47B	Greek Air Force
53-241	Nord 2501D Noratlas	Greek Air Force

Hungary

Bocsa

Petrol Station
Bócsa, 6235 Hungary

504	Lisunov Li-2 P	Hungarian Air Force

Budapest

Bokay Adventure Park
Budapest, Szélmalom u. 33, 1181 Hungary
www.bokaykalandpark.hu

HA-MDA	Antonov An-2R

Budapest Airport

P4-RMB	Boeing 737-291	Ground trainer
HA-LCA	Tupolev Tu-154 B2	Ex-Malev Ground trainer

Budapest Airport Aero Park
Budapest, BUD, 1185 Hungary

HA-MHI	Antonov An-2M	
HA-MDK	Antonov An-2R	
04 Red	Ilyushin IL-14T	Soviet Air Force

HA-MOA	Ilyushin IL-18V	Malev
HA-MOG	Ilyushin IL-18V	Malev Air Cargo
HA-LAF	LET 410 UVP E8A	
HA-LIQ	Lisunov Li-2 T	Malev
HA-LBE	Tupolev Tu-134	Malev
HA-LCG	Tupolev Tu-154 B2	Malev
HA-LRA	Yakovlev Yak-40	Linair
HA-YLR	Yakovlev Yak-40	Hungarian Aviation Authority

Csepel Technical School
Weiss Manfred ut, Csepel, Budapest, 1211 Hungary

HA-MHG	Antonov An-2M	Instructional airframe

Kerepesi Street, Budapest, 1106 Hungary

HA-MHU	Antonov An-2R	Mounted on poles, near McDonalds

Police Anti-Terrorist Training Centre
Budapest, Zách utca, 1101 Hungary

OM-CLB	Boeing 737-322	Ex-SkyEurope Airlines Visible from entrance on Pongrac ut

Polus Center
Budapest, Szentmihályi út 131, 1152 Hungary

HA-MDQ	Antonov An-2R	Outside McDonalds

Transport Museum
Budapest, Városligeti körút 11, 1146 Hungary
www.kozlekedesimuzeum.hu

| HA-ANJ | Antonov An-2 | |

Kecel

Military Museum and Technology Park
Kecel, Rákóczi Ferenc u. 177, 6237 Hungary
www.pintermuvek.hu

| 908 | Antonov AN-24B | Hungarian Air Force |

Szolnok

Reptar Szolnok Aviation Museum
Szolnok, Indóház u. 4-6, 5000 Hungary
www.reptar.hu
Some aircraft were still located at old museum site: Szolnok, Vitéz Tóth Lajos utca 1, 5008 Hungary

HA-MDG	Antonov An-2	Hungarian Air Force
907	Antonov An-24B	Hungarian Air Force
202	Antonov An-26	Hungarian Air Force
426	Ilyushin IL-14P	East German Air Force
HA-MOE	Ilyushin IL-18V	Malev
301	Lisunov Li-2P	Hungarian Air Force
HA-LBF	Tupolev Tu-134	Malev

Iceland

Icelandic Aviation Museum

Flugvallarvegur, Akureyri, Iceland
www.flugsafn.is

TF-JFA	Beech C-45H	
TF-FIE	Boeing 727-108C	Icelandair. Nose section
TF-ISM	DH.89 Dragon Rapide	
TF-IUB	Douglas DC-6A	Nose section
TF-SYN	Fokker F-27-200	Icelandic Coast Guard

Hnjotur Folk Museum

Orlygshofn 451, Hnjótur, Iceland
www.hnjotur.is

RA-50502	Antonov An-2TP	Aeroflot
17191	Douglas C-117D	US Navy Fuselage, wings and tail present alongside
TF-OAA	Douglas DC-6B	Nose section. Poor condition.

Hofn

Guest House
Birkifell, Hofn, Iceland

17281	Douglas C-117D	Used as summer house. Fuselage.

Reykjavik

Reykjavik Airport

TF-NPK	Douglas DC-3	Icelandair Airworthy

Ireland (Republic of)

Drumod

Cavan and Leitrim Railway
Station Road, Drumod, Co. Leitrim N41 R504, Ireland

VP-BDF	Boeing 707-321	Cockpit
G-AOIE	Douglas DC-7C	Forward fuselage

Dublin

Dublin Airport

EI-AOH	Vickers Viscount 803	Aer Lingus. Forward fuselage. Inside Aer Lingus Engineering hangar.
EI-CJD	Boeing 737-204	Ex-Ryanair. Instructional airframe.

Weston Airport

EI-BSF	Hawker Siddeley HS.748-1	Fuselage. Instructional airframe.

Enniscrone

Quirky Nights Glamping Village
Muckduff, Enniscrone, Co. Sligo, Ireland
quirkyglamping.town.ie

| EI-CZD | Boeing 767-216ER | Ex-Transaero. Fuselage used as a hostel. |

Shannon

Shannon Airport

| EI-CFA | Boeing 727-256 | Ground trainer |

Shannon Aviation Museum
Link Road, Shannon, Co. Clare, Ireland QPR97 SJ9
www.atlanticairadventures.com/shannon-aviation-musuem

G-AVMZ	BAC 1-11-510ED	Forward fuselage
C-GAPW	Boeing 737-275	Cockpit used as flight simulator.
G-CDPF	British Aerospace BAe 146	Ex-United Express N614AW. Cockpit.

Staffordstown

Dollys Grove Airstrip

| LY-AFO | Antonov An-2 | |

Italy

Borgo Faiti

Piana delle Orme Museum
Strada Migliara 43 1/2, 29, 04100 Latina LT, Italy
www.pianadelleorme.com

MM53-8146	Fairchild C-119J	Italian Air Force

Cameri

Air Force Base
Strada Statale Bellinzago, 28062 Località Aeroporto, Cameri NO, Italy

MM50-174	Grumman HU16A Albatross	Italian Air Force

Castelletto Sopra Ticino

Museo Gottard Park
Via Sempione, 172, 28053 Villaggi NO, Italy
www.museogottardpark.it

9868	Antonov An-2T	ex Polish Air Force

Corropoli

Corrorpoli Airfield
Via Brenta, 19, 64013 Corropoli TE, Italy

| MM61960 | Piaggio PD808 GE1 | Italian Air Force |

Fiumicino

Ristoaereo Restaurant
Via Trincea delle Frasche, 90, 00054 Fiumicino RM, Italy
www.ristoaereo.com

| MM61833 | Convair CV-440 | Italian Air Force |

Giglio

Mobil Rufa
03029 Sant'Angelo In Villa-giglio Province of Frosinone, Italy

| I-DABU | SE210 Caravelle 6N | Mounted on poles |

Guidona

Guidona Airport
Viale Roma, 26, 00012 Guidonia RM, Italy

| MM61734 | Beech C-45F | Italian Air Force |

Lampedusa

Lampedusa Airport
Contrada Cala Francese, Lampedusa, AG 92010, 92010 Lampedusa e Linosa AG, Italy

MM50-177	Grumman HU16A Albatross	Italian Air Force

La Spezia

Cadimare Military Base
Via della Marina, 15, 19131 Cadimare, La Spezia SP, Italy

MM61948	Piaggio PD808 VIP	Italian Air Force

Lucca

Viale Europa, 750, 55100 Lucca LU, Italy

MM62014	Piaggio PD808 RM	Italian Air Force Mounted on roundabout near A11 autostrada

Milan

Air Ambulance
Via Peppino Rossi, 23, 20093 Cologno Monzese MI, Italy
www.airambulance.it

N565SS	Cessna Citation 1	Fuselage Air ambulance simulator

Volandia Museum

Via per Tornavento, 15, 21019 Somma Lombardo VA, Italy
www.volandia.it

Unmarked	Dornier D328jet	Fuselage
I-RAGF	Douglas DC-3	
MM62012	Douglas DC-9-32	Italian Air Force
I-MLXT	Fokker F27-500	Miniliner
I-SMEL	McDonnell Douglas MD-82	Meridiana

Montagnana

Museo del Volo

Via Rotta Vecchia, 8, 35044 Montagnana PD, Italy

I-MLGT	Fokker F27-500	Miniliner

Olbia

Olbia Airport

MM61743	Beech C-45F (Expeditor 11)	Hanging inside terminal Marked I-SARE

Ostia

I.T.I. Faraday

Via Capo Sperone, 52, 00122 Lido di Ostia RM, Italy
www.itifaraday.gov.it

MM61952	Piaggio PD808 TP	Italian Air Force

Parma

Parma Airport

MM61955	Piaggio PD808 TP	Italian Air Force Mounted on poles

Pisa

Pisa Airport

MM53-3200	Fairchild C-119F	Italian Air Force
MM62110	Fiat G222 TCM	Italian Air Force To become gate guard

Pompeii

Hotel Imperiale
Via Panoramica, 1, 80040 Terzigno NA, Italy
www.hotelimperiale.it

MM61722	Beech C-45F	Italian Air Force

Pratica di Mare

Aeroporto Militare Mario de Bernardi

MM61893	Douglas DC-3	Italian Air Force Marked MM61775
MM62016	Piaggio PD808 RM	Italian Air Force
MM61957	Piaggio PD808 TP	Italian Air Force
MM61958	Piaggio PD808 GE1	Italian Air Force

Rimini

Museo dell'Aviazione Theme Park
Via Santa Aquilina, 58, 47900 Rimini RN, Italy
www.museoaviazione.com

SP-TCD	Antonov An-2R	
SP-TCG	Antonov An-2R	Wears false Croatian Air Force marks
N242AG	Douglas DC-3 R4D-5	
MM61826	Douglas DC-3	Italian Air Force
OK-FDC	LET-410 M	Wears false Czech Air Force marks
I-NARW	Swearingen Merlin Lva	

Rivolto

Rivolto Air Base

MM52-6020	Fairchild C-119J Boxcar	Italian Air Force

Rome

Ciampino Airport
Via Appia Nuova, 1651, 00040 Roma RM, Italy

MM51-035	Grumman HU16A Albatross	Italian Air Force Gate Guard near terminal
MM61950	Piaggio PD808 VIP	Italian Air Force

Istituto Tecnico Aeronautico
Via Francesco Morandini, 30, 00142 Roma RM, Italy

I-LIRG	Vickers Viscount 798D	Technical trainer

Roveredo in Piano

33074 Fontanafredda, Province of Pordenone, Italy

I-DABM	Sud SE.210 Caravelle 6N	Alitalia

Sant'Egidio alla Vibrata

Pizzeria Ristorante Caravelle
Via Metella, 40, 64016 Sant'Egidio alla Vibrata TE, Italy

I-GISE	SE.210 Caravelle 3	Restaurant

Seriate

Via Basse, 24068 Seriate BG, Italy

MM61895	Douglas DC-3	Italian Air Force Near Bergamo Airport

Sicily

Air Pub Café
Zona Industriale San Cataldo Scalo, 93100 Caltanissetta CL, Italy

5N-KAY	Douglas DC-9-32	Fuselage used as restaurant

Turin

Turin Airport

| N8383 | Douglas DC-3 | Marked I-LEON
Mounted on poles |

Udine

Technical School

| MM61755 | Beech C-45F | Italian Air Force |

Vermicino

Restaurant Zi Pietro
Via Tuscolana, 1713, 00173 Roma RM, Italy
www.ristorantepizzeriazipietro.it

| MM61677 | Beech C-45F | Wears false US Air Force
marks
Mounted on a pole |

Vigna di Valle

Museo Storico Aeronautica Militare
Via Circumlacuale, 00062 Vigna di Valle, Bracciano RM, Italy
aeronautica.difesa.it

MM61776	Douglas DC-3	Italian Air Force
MM50-179	Grumman HU16A Albatross	Italian Air Force
MM61961	Piaggio PD808 GE1	Italian Air Force

Villamarzana

Via Frattesina, off S434, 45030 San Bellino RO, Italy

MM61965	Douglas DC-6B	Italian Air Force
OK-CFE	Tupolev Tu-134A	CSA Czech Airlines

Kazakhstan

Aktobe

Military Museum
A. Moldagulova Ave 39, Aktobe 030012, Kazakhstan

CCCP-11985	Antonov An-12BP	Kazakhstan Air Force
01 Yellow	Antonov An-26	Kazakhstan Air Force
CCC9-87590	Yakovlev Yak-40	Kazakhstan Air Force

Astana

020000, Astana 010000, Kazakhstan

UN-46334	Antonov An-26B	Mounted on poles next to lake Behind Agat Hotel Astana

Atyrau

Atyrau Airport

UN-47737	Antonov An-24B	ex Air Kazakstan Preserved next to airport access road

Baikonur

Samolet An-12, Aviatsionnaya Street, Baikonur, Kazakhstan

14 Blue	Antonov An-12AP	Soviet Air Force Mounted on platform in city street

Kostanay

Kostanay Airport

UN-67466	LET-410 UVP	Ex-Aeroflot Parked in front of terminal

Merki

CCCP-75813	Ilyushin IL-18V	Aeroflot Parked on M39 main road to east of city centre

Oskemen

Etno Park / Ethnographic Museum

A-350, Ust'-Kamenogorsk 070000, Kazakhstan
www.vkoem.kz

CCCP-43973	Antonov An-2P	
CCCP-87492	Yakovlev Yak-40	Air Kazakhstan

Semey

Semey Airport
Semey 070000, Kazakhstan

UN-88259	Yakovlev Yak-40	SemeyAvia On platform outside terminal.

Shymkent

Zhybek Zholy St 30, Shymkent, Kazakhstan

UN-46289	Antonov An-26B	Air Kazakhstan Formerly a cafe

Stepnyak

Stepnyak 020000

CCCP-87749	Yakovlev Yak-40	Ex-Aeroflot On plinths near centre of town.

Tulkbas

CCCP-46749	Antonov An-26	Ex-Aeroflot On private grounds

Ust-Kamenogorsk

Metallurg Park
Ulitsa Stakhanovskaya, Ust'-Kamenogorsk 070000, Kazakhstan

CCCP-87498	Yakovlev Yak-40	Air Kazakhstan

Ust-Kamenogorsk Airport

CCCP-61692	Avia-14M	Ex-Aeroflot Parked at southern end of airport.

Zhezkazgan

Zhezkazgan Airport
Bul'var Garyshkeler Dvukhstoroniy 34, Zhezqazghan 100000, Kazakhstan

UN-67407	LET-410 UVP	Parked in front of terminal.

Latvia

Ciemupe

Dakota Restaurant
Priežu iela 1, Ciemupe, Ogresgala pagasts, LV-5041, Latvia

07 Yellow	Antonov An-2R	Latvian Air Force
YL-LCA	Antonov An-24B	Nose

Limbazi

Limbazi Airport
Langači-Limbažu lidlauks, Limbažu pagasts, LV-4001 Latvia

YL-LEF	Antonov An-2R	ex Soviet Air Force

Riga

Riga Aviation Museum
Riga International Airport, LV-1053, Latvia
www.airmuseum.lv

22 Yellow	Antonov An-2TD	Soviet Air Force
01 Red	Antonov An-14A	Soviet Air Force Fuselage
YL-LCD	Antonov An-24B	Latavio
YL-KAE	LET 410 UVP	Concors

CCCP-42328	Tupolev Tu-104A	Aeroflot Nose section
CCCP-45052	Tupolev Tu-124B	Aeroflot Nose section
RA-65717	Tupolev Tu-134A-3	Aeroflot
CCCP-65698	Tupolev Tu-134B	Aeroflot Nose section

Riga International Airport

CCCP-65874	Tupolev Tu-134A	Fire trainer

Tukums

Tukums Airport

YL-CAO	Antonov An-2TD
3X-GGU	Ilyushin IL-18D
LY-AAC	Yakovlev Yak-40

Lithuania

Kaunas

Lithuanian Aircraft Museum
Veiverių g. 132, Kaunas 46338, Lithuania
www.lam.lt

4184	Antonov An-2P	Polish Air Force
CCCP-70224	Antonov An-2R	
06 Yellow	Antonov An-24B	Lithuanian Air Force
34 Red	Antonov An-14	Soviet Air Force Missing outer wings

Vilnius

Amikon Aviation Training
Meistrų g. 8, Vilnius 02189, Lithuania

XX486	Handley Page Jetstream T.2	Fuselage. Inside technical college.

Malta

Malta Airport

5N-BBQ	BAC 1-11 520FN	Ground trainer
9L-LDJ	BAC 1-11 531 FS	Ground trainer

Ta Qali

Malta Aviation Museum
Attard, Malta
www.maltaaviationmuseum.com

N495F	Beech C-45H	Under restoration
5N-BBP	BAC 1-11 518FG	Nose section
C-FITH	Douglas DC-3	
T9-ABC	Douglas DC-3	

Moldova

Chisinau

Chisinau Airport

ER-65036	Tupolev TU-134A-3	Air Moldova Mounted on poles outside terminal

Netherlands

Amsterdam Schiphol Airport

PH-PBA	Douglas DC-3	Dutch Dakota Association. Airworthy
N929L	Douglas DC-9-32	Forward fuselage. Wears false KLM colours. Located inside terminal before security.
PH-OFE	Fokker 100	KLM Cityhopper. Mounted on Panorama Terrace.
N19XE	Fokker F27-500	Fokker. Marked PH-NIV. Mounted on poles over lake close to RW16L, at 1438 AM Oude Meer.
N555LB	Learjet 24	Modified into playground slide. In terminal departure lounge. Wears false KLM colours.

MBO College – ROC van Amsterdam
Opaallaan 25, 2132 XV Hoofddorp, Netherlands
www.rocva.nl

N768KM	Boeing 737-287	Ex-Aerolineas Argentinas Marked PH-ROC Instructional airframe
VP-BRQ	Boeing 737-528	Fuselage Ex-Yamal Airlines Instructional airframe

G-BDXO	Boeing 747-236	Cockpit
TF-ODM	Handley Page Jetstream 1	Instructional airframe
TF-ODN	Handley Page Jetstream 1	Instructional airframe

The Aviation Megastore
Molenweg 249, 1436 BV Aalsmeerderbrug, Netherlands
www.aviationmegastore.com

| G-BPMP | Douglas C-47A | Cockpit
Marked 42-24211 |

Baarlo

PS Aero
Napoleonsbaan Zuid 27C, 5991 NB Baarlo, Netherlands
www.psaero.com

61+11	Breguet 1150/1151 Atlantic	West German Air Force
F-BTTJ	Dassault Mercure 100	Air Inter. Forward fuselage.
D-BAKH	Fokker F27-200	Ex-WDL. Forward fuselage.
AP-BHZ	Fokker F27-500	
XX481	Handley Page Jetstream T.2	Royal Navy
F-BHRA	Sud SE.210 Caravelle 3	Air France

Eindhoven

Eindhoven Airport
Flight Forum 1950, 5657 EZ Eindhoven, Netherlands

C-8	Fokker F27-300M	Royal Netherlands Air Force. Preserved next to road near Parkeerplaats Park Meerhoven.

Lelystad

Luchtvaart-Theme Park Aviodrome
Pelikaanweg 50, 8218 PG Lelystad, Netherlands
www.aviodrome.nl

562 Red	Antonov An-2R	
V-29	Beech C-45G	Royal Netherlands Air Force
PH-BUK	Boeing 747-206(SUD)	KLM
PH-PBY	Consolidated PBY Catalina 5A	Airworthy
PH-MAD	De Havilland DH104 Devon C.20	Martins Air Charter
OO-SCD	De Havilland DH104 Dove 6	Cockpit. Martins Air Charter
PH-ALR	Douglas C-47B	Holland titles
PH-TCB	Douglas C-47A	KLM
PH-DDY	Douglas C-54A	Netherlands Government
N39165	Douglas DC-2	Marked PH-AJU
PH-DDZ	Douglas DC-3	Martins Air Charter Airworthy
H-NADP	Fokker F.VII	KLM
PH-FHF	Fokker F27-100	NLM
PH-NIV	Fokker F27-100	Rear fuselage

PH-NVF	Fokker F27-100	Fokker
PH-OSI	Fokker 50	Fokker. Prototype.
PH-MKC	Fokker 70	Cockpit
PH-OFA	Fokker 100	KLM Cityhopper
151	Grumman US-2N Tracker	Wears KLM colours
159	Grumman US-2N Tracker	Royal Netherlands Navy
1Z+IK	Junkers Ju52	
210	Lockheed SP-2H Neptune	Royal Netherlands Air Force
N749NL	Lockheed VC-121B Constellation	KLM. Airworthy.
PH-TRO	Sud SE.210 Caravelle 3	Cockpit. Transavia

Maastricht

Aviation Competence Centre
Horsterweg 13, 6199 AC Maastricht-Airport, Netherlands
www.aviationcompetencecentre.nl

G-TNTD	British Aerospace BAe 146-200(QT)	Cockpit
LX-N20199	Boeing 707-329C TCA	Centre fuselage section

Soesterberg

National Military Museum
Verlengde Paltzerweg 1, 3768 MX Soest, Netherlands
www.nmm.nl

G-10	Beech D-18S	Royal Netherlands Air Force
BV-3	De Havilland DH89 Dragon Rapide	Royal Netherlands Air Force

S-6	De Havilland Canada DHC-2 Beaver	Royal Netherlands Air Force
T-443	Douglas C-47A	Royal Netherlands Air Force
C-10	Fokker F27-300M	Royal Netherlands Air Force
16-212	PBY Catalina	Royal Netherlands Navy

Teuge

Hotelsuites
De Zanden 61b, 7395 PA Teuge, Netherlands
www.hotelsuites.nl

| DDR-STD | Ilyushin IL-18V | Used as a hotel |

Utrecht

Multi Pilot Simulations
Kon. Wilhelminaweg 449, 3737 BE Groenekan, Netherlands
www.mps.aero

| 2100847 | Douglas C-47B | Cockpit. Used as a simulator. |

Woensdrecht

Bed & Breakfast Domaine Haute Bruyere
Nijverheidstraat 28, 4631 KS Hoogerheide, Netherlands
www.horstinkwijn.nl

| PH-FCX | Fokker F27-400MPA | Used as hotel room |

Norway

Bodø

Norwegian Aviation Museum
Olav V gate, 8004 Bodø, Norway
luftfart.museum.no

LN-KKW	Boeing 737-3K9	Norwegian
LN-LMN	De Havilland Canada DHC-6 Twin Otter	Widerøe
LN-SUC	Fokker F28-1000	Braathens S.A.F.E.
N16SK	Rockwell Jet Commander 1121	
6306	Junkers Ju52	Marked LN-DAF
CO+EI	Junkers Ju52	Luftwaffe. Preserved in wrecked state.
C-FIZO	PBY-6A Catalina	Wears false Royal Air Force colours. Marked FP535.

Kjeller

Skedsmo High School
Vestbygata 61, 2003 Lillestrøm, Norway

N870BB	Beech 400A	Instructional airframe

Kristiansand

Kristiansand Airport Air Force Training Centre

LN-FAJ	British Aerospace Jetstream 31-02	Instructional airframe
LN-FAV	British Aerospace Jetstream 31-02	Instructional airframe

Oslo

Norsk Teknisk Museum
Kjelsåsveien 143, 0491 Oslo, Norway
www.tekniskmuseum.no

LN-KLH	Sud SE.210 Caravelle 3	SAS Scandinavian Airlines

Norwegian Armed Forces Aircraft Collection
Museumsvegen 35, 2060 Gardermoen, Norway
www.flysam.no

7062	De Havilland Canada DHC-6 Twin Otter	Royal Norwegian Air Force
93797	Douglas C-47A	Royal Norwegian Air Force
CA+JY	Junkers Ju52	Luftwaffe
953	Lockheed C-130H Hercules	Royal Norwegian Air Force
N283M	Lockheed Lodestar	Wears false BOAC colours. Marked G-AGIH.

Sandefjord

Sandefjord Airport

LN-WND	Douglas C-53D	Dakota Norway. Airworthy.

Stavanger

Flyhistorisk Museum
Flyplassveien 131, 4050 Sola, Norway
www.jaermuseet.no

LN-MAF	Britten Norman BN.2A-21 Islander	Norvings A/S
LN-KLK	Convair CV-440	Nor-Fly
LN-BFY	De Havilland DH.114 Heron	Braathens S.A.F.E. Marked LN-PSG
LN-SUF	Fokker F27-100	Braathens S.A.F.E.
LN-HAL	Grumman G-44 Widgeon	
L-587	PBY-5A Catalina	Royal Danish Air Force. Marked '382'

Poland

Biedrusko

Palace Restaurant Biedrusko
62-003 Biedrusko; 1 Maja 86, 62-003 Biedrusko, Poland

SP-ANT	Antonov An-2TD	ex Polish Air Force Next to minor road.

Bobrek

Petrol Station ORLEN
Krakowska 96, 32-661 Bobrek, Poland

7449	Antonov An-2	ex Polish Air Force

Brzeźnica

Wiślana 43, 34-114 Brzeźnica, Poland

032	Yakovlev Yak-40	Polish Air Force In field beside road.

Chlapowo

Alexa Camping
aleja Żeromskiego 44, 84-120 Władysławowo, Poland
alexa.gda.pl

SP-LHG	Tupolev Tu-134A	LOT Polish Airlines Used as a restaurant

Czestochowa

Jagiellońska, 42-200 Częstochowa, Poland

1603	Antonov An-26	Polish Air Force

Deblin

Polish Air Force Museum
Lotników Polskich 1, 08-530 Dęblin, Poland
www.muzeumsp.pl

7810	Antonov An-2P	Polish Air Force
7448	Antonov An-2T	Polish Air Force In poor condition.
9866	Antonov An-2T	Polish Air Force In poor condition.
0916	Ilyushin IL-14P	Polish Air Force
045	Yakovlev Yak-40	Polish Air Force
048	Yakovlev Yak-40	Polish Air Force

Drzonow

Lubuskie Military Museum
Drzonów 54, 66-008 Świdnica, Poland
museum.drzonow.eu

SP-LAS	Lisunov Li-2	LOT Polish Airlines
3069	Ilyushin IL-14P	Polish Air Force

Garczegorze

BP Petrol Station
Garczegorze 60A, 84-351 Nowa Wieś Lęborska, Poland

1316	Antonov An-2M	Polish Air Force

Koscielec

Airplan Restaurant
Mykanowska 25, 42-240 Kościelec, Poland
www.zajazd-wysoczanski.com.pl

SP-LSD	Ilyushin IL-18V	Used as a restaurant

Koszalin

Museum of Antiaircraft Defense
Wojska Polskiego 70, 75-903 Koszalin, Poland
www.muzeumsp.pl

047	Yakovlev Yak-40	Polish Air Force

Krakow

Krakow Airport Military Base

1403	Antonov An-26	Polish Air Force

Polish Aviation Museum
al. Jana Pawła II 39, 31-864 Kraków, Poland
www.muzeumlotnictwa.pl

6316	Amiot AAC-1 (Ju52)	Luftwaffe Marked IZ+NK
SP-WMK	Antonov An-2R	
5705	Antonov An-2T	Polish Air Force Fuselage
1508	Antonov An-26	Polish Air Force
027	Lisunov Li-2	Polish Air Force
3078	Ilyushin IL-14P	Polish Air Force
SP-PBL	PZL MD12F	
SP-LHB	Tupolev Tu-134A	LOT Polish Airlines
037	Yakovlev Yak-40	Polish Air Force

Krosno

Podkarpacki Airfield
Franciszka Żwirki i Stanisława Wigury 8, 38-400 Krosno, Poland

SP-CNF	Antonov An-2T	Marked 'CNF 1450'

Luban

Central School of the Border Guards

1406	Antonov An-26	Polish Air Force Ground trainer

Mielec

Legionów 80, 39-300 Mielec, Poland

SP-WNL	Antonov An-2R	'Welcome to Mielec' titles On 984 road at edge of town.

Powidz

Powidz Air Base

1507	Lockheed C-130E Hercules	Polish Air Force Ground trainer.

Poznan

Muzeum Uzbrojenia
aleja Armii Poznań, 60-101 Poznań, Poland

9863	Antonov An-2T	Polish Air Force

Zerniki-Gadki Airfield
Poznańska 3, 62-023 Gądki, Poland

N513GL	Douglas DC-3	Mounted on poles

Rudzienice

1317	Antonov An-2R	Polish Air Force Near 16 road.

Stare Olesno

Holiday Resort ANPOL
Kolejowa 2, 46-300 Olesno, Poland

SP-LTC	Antonov An-26B	On island in lake

Skarzysko-Kamienna

Orla Bialego Museum
Słoneczna 90, 26-110 Skarżysko-Kamienna, Poland

3054	Ilyushin IL-14P	Polish Air Force

Strumien

Petrol Station ORLEN
1-go Maja 69, 43-246 Zbytków, Poland

SP-LSH	Ilyushin IL-18GR	Coca-Cola colours

Strysza Buda

Kaszubski Park Gigantow
Kartuska 30, 83-329 Strysza Buda, Poland
www.parkgigantow.pl

SP-LHF	Tupolev Tu-134A	LOT Polish Airlines

Szreniawa

National Museum of Agriculture and Food Industry
Dworcowa 5, 62-052 Szreniawa, Poland

SP-WMF	Antonov An-2R	

Warsaw

Military University of Technology in Warsaw
gen. Witolda Urbanowicza 2, 01-476 Warszawa, Poland
wat.edu.pl

042	Yakovlev Yak-40	Polish Air Force Parked in compound next to Radiowa road and Goldwings Flight Academy (connected to Lotnisko Airfield).

Museum of the Polish Army
Aleje Jerozolimskie 3, 00-495 Warszawa, Poland
www.muzeumwp.pl

5928	Antonov An-2P	Polish Air Force
1602	Antonov An-26	Polish Air Force
044	Yakovlev Yak-40	Polish Air Force

Warsaw Frederic Chopin Airport

SP-TWF	Antonov An-2TP	Western side of airport, off Aleja Krakowska
SP-LTA	Antonov An-26B	LOT Polish Airlines Poor condition.
SP-LNE	Ilyushin IL-14P	LOT Polish Airlines In poor condition, fuselage of SP-LNB is adjacent.

Wieruszów

Public Park
Al. Turystyczna, 98-400 Wieruszów, Poland

SP-LKI	Lisunov Li-2	LOT Polish Airlines Mounted on plinths.

Wroclaw

University of Science and Technology
wybrzeże Stanisława Wyspiańskiego 27, 50-370 Wrocław, Poland

1853	Antonov An-2T	Ground trainer

Portugal

Alverca

Air Museum (Museu do Ar)
Rua do Largo dos Pioneiros da Aviação, 2615-174 Alverca do Ribatejo, Portugal
www.emfa.pt

| 129 | Grumman Widgeon G-44 | Portuguese Navy |

Evora

Aeródromo de Évora
Estr. de Viana, 7005-210 Évora, Portugal

| 3C-JJO | Convair CV-440 | SOTIP |

Leiria

Municipal Park
Rua Comissão de Iniciativa 4B, 2400-137 Leiria, Portugal

| 2508 | Beech C-45 Expeditor | Portuguese Air Force |

Lisbon

KidZania
Dolce Vita Mall, Avenida Cruzeiro Seixas 5 e 7, 2650 Amadora, Portugal

	Douglas DC-9	Forward fuselage mounted next to KidZania entrance. Reg unknown.

Montijo Air Base

14802	Lockheed P3P Orion	Portuguese Air Force Ground trainer

Naval Museum
Praça do Império, 1400-206 Lisboa, Portugal
museu.marinha.pt

120	Grumman Widgeon G-44	Portuguese Navy Marked as '128'

Ota

Technical School
Estr. da Base Aérea, Portugal

16510	CASA 212	Portuguese Air Force Ground trainer
CR-CAL	De Havilland DH 104 Dove	ex DETA Mozambique Being restored.

Ovar

Aerodromo de Manobra Museum
Rua da Base Aérea, 3885-718 Maceda, Portugal
www.emfa.pt

16503	CASA 212	Portuguese Air Force

Sintra

Air Museum (Museu do Ar)
2715-021 Pêro Pinheiro, Portugal
www.museudoar.pt

CS-TBD	Boeing 707-328B	TAP Air Portugal Nose section
16508	CASA 212	Portuguese Air Force
17103	Dassault Falcon 20DC	Portuguese Air Force
2307	De Havilland DH 89A Dragon Rapide	Portuguese Air Force
CS-DGA	Douglas DC-3	TAP Air Portugal Marked CS-TDA on one side
6304	Junkers Ju-52 3m3ge	Portuguese Air Force
5T-TAK	Lockheed L-1049G Super Constellation	Forward fuselage Used in Biafran Relief operation, registration not official.
14806	Lockheed P-3P Orion	Portuguese Air Force
6405	Nord N2502A Noratlas	Portuguese Air Force

Tancos

Tancos Air Base
Praia do Ribatejo, Portugal

16507	CASA 212	Portuguese Air Force Gate guardian. Mounted on poles, nose down.

Romania

Bucharest

Baneasa Airport
Aviation Technical College
Bulevardul Ficusului 44, București 077190, Romania

YR-AMC	Antonov An-24RV	TAROM
TN-BZC	BAC 1-11-488GH	Used as part of office complex

MOL Petrol Station
Șoseaua Colentina 258-260, București 021191, Romania

YR-PBV	Antonov An-2R	Primaria Sectorului Mounted on traffic roundabout outside petrol station.

Otopeni Airport

5024	Antonov An-24RT	Romanian Air Force Gate guard outside military part of airport.

Romanian Aviation Museum
Șoseaua Fabrica de Glucoză, București 077190, Romania

130	Britten Norman BN-2A Islander	Romanian Air Force

Buzias

La Aeroport Restaurant
Strada Principală 15, Buziaș 305100, Romania
www.aeroportbuzias.ro

1004	Lisunov Li-2	ex Romanian Air Force Used as Bar/Restaurant

Craiova

Craiova University
Faculty of Electrotechcnica
Bulevardul Decebal 107, Craiova 200440, Romania

YR-AMX	Antonov An-24V	Marked YR-FEL

Faget

Strade Gheorghe Doja

209	Lisunov Li-2	ex Romanian Air Force Next to road at eastern end of town.

Orastie

Aventure Park Arsenal
Strada Codrului 27, Orăștie 335700, Romania
www.aventura-park.ro

YR-PVA	Antonov An-2R

Ploiesti

West Park
Ariceştii Rahtivani, Romania

5N-TSA	Boeing 737-2H4	Ploiesti West Park Parked next to roundabout

Pucioasa

Clubul Copiilor Mateescu Nicolae
Strada C. Olănescu 19, Pucioasa 135400, Romania

YR-BMC	Antonov An-24RV	TAROM Part of a school

Suceava

Suceava Airport
Strada Aeroportului, Salcea 727475, Romania

YR-PMJ	Antonov An-2R	Bucovina Fly Club Marked YR-SCV, mounted on poles.

Timisoara

Aviatia Utilitara Airfield

YR-PSB	Antonov An-2R

Russia

This list includes Western Russia, taking in the major areas of population around Moscow and St. Petersburg, and in proximity to Eastern Europe.

Anapa

Anapa Airport

RA-87572	Yakovlev Yak-40	Next to control tower

Bryansk

Belo-Berezhskiy Airport
Авиаторов ул., 1/1, Oktyabr'skoye, Bryanskaya oblast', Russia, 241522

RA-71208	Antonov An-2R	Soviet Air Force

Dubna

Bol'shaya Volga
Tver Oblast, Russia, 171291

RA-85467	Tupolev Tu-154B-2	Ex-Eurasia. Instructional airframe.

Shore of Domkinski Zaliv Bay

CCCP-42537	Yakovlev Yak-42	Ex-Aeroflot. No engines.

Dyatkovo

Cadet School

Ulitsa Tsiolkovskogo, 7, Dyatkovo, Bryanskaya oblast', Russia, 242600

RA-87373	Yakovlev Yak-40	Ex-Bravia

Gelendzhik

Gelendzhik Airport

Solntsedarskaya Ulitsa, 10, Gelendzhik, Krasnodarskiy kray, Russia, 353468

RA-42350	Yakovlev Yak-42	Ex-Kuban Airlines. Instructional airframe.

Kazan

Kazanskiy Natsional'nyy Issledovatel'skiy Tekhnicheskiy Universitet Im. A.n. Tupoleva

Ulitsa Chetayeva, 18, Kazan, Respublika Tatarstan, Russia, 420126
www.kai.ru

CCCP-77107	Tupolev Tu-144S	Aeroflot

Kimry

Pamyatnik Samoletu Tu-124

Kommunisticheskaya Ulitsa, 2/5, Kimry, Tverskaya oblast', Russia, 171504

CCCP-64452	Tupolev Tu-124V	Aeroflot

Kubinka

Patriot Park
Минское ш., Moskovskaya oblast', Russia, 143063
www.patriotp.ru

11 Yellow	Antonov An-2	Soviet Air Force

Kurchatov-Dichnya

Holiday Park Rakhol
Урочище Рахоль, владение 13, Dichnya, Russia, 307236
www.rakhol.ru

CCCP-75568	Ilyushin IL-18Gr	Aeroflot

Ladozhskoye Ozero

Doroga Zhizni, Filial Tsentral'nogo Voyenno-Morskogo Museum
Ladozhskoye Ozero, Leningradskaya oblast', Russia, 188675
www.doroga-zhizni.ru

4681	Lisunov Li-2	Soviet Air Force

Lobnya

Bashnya Shukhova
Lobnya, Moscow Oblast, Russia, 141055

CCCP-41326	Antonov An-2

Moscow

All-Russian Exhibition Center
Prospekt Mira, 119, Moskva, Russia, 129223
www.vdnh.ru

CCCP-42304	Yakovlev Yak-42	Marked RA-19751

Aviapark Shopping Centre
Khodynskiy Bul'var, 4, Moskva, Russia, 125167

RA-65694	Tupolev Tu-134B-3	Parked on north-western corner of shopping centre.
OK-UCE	Tupolev Tu-154M	Forward fuselage mounted next to KidZania entrance.

Central Museum of the Air Force
Muzeynaya Ulitsa, 2, Monino, Moskovskaya oblast', Russia, 141170
www.cmaf.ru

10 Green	Antonov An-8	Soviet Air Force
CCCP-11213	Antonov An-10A	Aeroflot
04 Red	Antonov An-12	Soviet Air Force
01 Red	Antonov An-14	Soviet Air Force
CCCP-09334	Antonov An-22	Wears false Aeroflot titles
CCCP-46746	Antonov An-24	
10 Red	Ilyushin IL-12	Soviet Air Force
CCCP-75737	Ilyushin IL-18V	Aeroflot
CCCP-86670	Ilyushin IL-62	Aeroflot
CCCP-86047	Ilyushin IL-76	Soviet Air Force
RA-86095	Ilyushin IL-86	Aeroflot. Cockpit.

39 Yellow	Lisunov Li-2	Soviet Air Force
CCCP-93914	Lisunov Li-2T	Aeroflot
46 Red	Tupolev Tu-104AK	Soviet Air Force
CCCP-L5611	Tupolev Tu-114	Aeroflot
CCCP-45025	Tupolev Tu-124	Aeroflot. Fuselage damaged by fire.
CCCP-77106	Tupolev Tu-144	Aeroflot
CCCP-87490	Yakovlev Yak-40	Aeroflot
CCCP-42302	Yakovlev Yak-42	Aeroflot

Dolgoprudnenskiy Aviatsionnyy Tekhnikum
Ploshchad' Sobina, 1, Dolgoprudny, Moskovskaya oblast', Russia, 141701

CCCP-64458	Antonov An-2M	Aeroflot

Lytkarino, near Myachkovo Airfield
Lytkarino, Moscow Oblast, Russia, 140123

RA-30043	Antonov An-30	Ex-Aeroflot. Mounted on poles.

Moscow Aviation Institute
Moscow, Russia, 125080

CCCP-19661	Yakovlev Yak-40	Instructional airframe

Ostafyevo Airport
поселение Рязановское, Moscow, Moskovskaya oblast', Russia

07 Yellow	Ilyushin IL-14T	Soviet Air Force

Shremetyevo Airport
Sheremetyevskoye shosse, Moscow, Russia, 141425

CCCP-86492	Ilyushin IL-62M	Aeroflot. Mounted on plinths north side of airport.
RA-96005	Ilyushin IL-96-300	Ex-Aeroflot. Ground trainer.

Victory Park
пл. Победы, 3Г, Moskva, Russia, 119590

42 Red	Antonov An-12BP	Soviet Air Force
17 Yellow	Lisunov Li-2T	Soviet Air Force

Vnukovo Airport
Vnukovo, Moscow, Russia, 119027

CCCP-42507	Tupolev Tu-104B	Marked CCCP-L5412. Mounted on plinth near airport entrance road.

Rybinsk

City Centre
Ulitsa Motorostroiteley, 5, Rybinsk, Yaroslavskaya oblast', Russia, 152931

CCCP-42460	Tupolev Tu-104A	Aeroflot. Mounted on concrete plinth.

St. Petersburg

Levashovo Airbase
Gorskoye sh., Levashovo, Sankt-Peterburg, Russia, 194361

03 Red	Antonov An-24B	Soviet Air Force. Marked 33 Red.

Karavayevskaya Ulitsa
Karavayevskaya Ulitsa, 46, Sankt-Peterburg, Russia, 192177

RA-65144	Tupolev Tu-134A-3	Ex-Rossiya. Ground trainer.

Seretino

Beside 14-K4 west of town

RA-87550	Yakovlev Yak-40

Shakhty

Cadet Corps
Sel'skaya Ulitsa, 42, Shakhty, Rostovskaya oblast', Russia, 346503

RA-85400	Tupolev Tu-154B-2	Cockpit

Smolensk

Corner of Frunze/Ulitsa roads

CCCP-10985	Yakovlev Yak-42	Aeroflot. Mounted on concrete plinths.

Stavropol

Park Pobedy
Shpakovskaya ulitsa, 111, Stavropol, Stavropolskiy kray, Russia, 355040
www.stavparks.ru

CCCP-75767	Ilyushin IL-18V	Part of amusement ground

Temryuk

Military Hill Museum
Ulitsa Lyuksemburg, Temryuk, Krasnodarskiy kray, Russia, 353507

CCCP-46791	Antonov An-24B	Ex-Aeroflot

Ulyanovsk

Museum of Civil Aviation
ул. Авиационная, 20 A, Ulyanovsk, Ulyanovskaya oblast', Russia, 433327
www.uvauga.ru

RA-40561	Antonov An-2TP	
CCCP-48104	Antonov An-14	Aeroflot
CCCP-46761	Antonov An-24	Aeroflot
RA-26503	Antonov An-26	
CCCP-91588	Ilyushin IL-14M	Aeroflot
CCCP-6132	Ilyushin IL-14P	Aeroflot
CCCP-74250	Ilyushin IL-18D	Aeroflot
CCCP-86650	Ilyushin IL-62	Aeroflot
RA-86507	Ilyushin IL-62M	Aeroflot
RA-86062	Ilyushin IL-86	Atlant Soyuz Airlines

CCCP-67252	LET 410	Aeroflot
RA-15122	Myasischev M101T	
CCCP-H317	Tupolev ANT-4	
CCCP-42322	Tupolev Tu-104	Aeroflot
CCCP-76490	Tupolev Tu-114	Aeroflot
CCCP-45017	Tupolev Tu-124Sh	Aeroflot
CCCP-65748	Tupolev Tu-134AK	Aeroflot
CCCP-77110	Tupolev Tu-144S	Aeroflot
RA-85061	Tupolev Tu-154B	
RA-85470	Tupolev Tu-154B-2	
RA-87299	Yakovlev Yak-40	Aeroflot
RA-87357	Yakovlev Yak-40	Volga-Dnepr
RA-87653	Yakovlev Yak-40	
RA-42539	Yakovlev Yak-42	Kapat

Vologda

Vologda Airport

CCCP-75518	Ilyushin IL-18V	Aeroflot. Outside terminal.

Voronezh-Chertovitskoye

Voronezh Airport
территория Аэропорт, Voronezh, Voronezhskaya oblast', Russia, 394025

RA-65880	Tupolev Tu-134A-3	Parked near terminal car park

Vyazma

Dvoyevka Airfield
Smolensk Oblast, Russia, 215107

| 54 Red | Antonov An-24T | Instructional airframe |

Yegoryevsk

Atb Yeatk Ga
Ulitsa Bronnitskaya, 23, Yegoryevsk, Moskovskaya oblast', Russia, 140301

CCCP-01759	Antonov An-2P	Instructional airframe
CCCP-01760	Antonov An-2P	Instructional airframe
CCCP-46745	Antonov An-24	Instructional airframe
RA-46409	Antonov An-24B	Instructional airframe
TZ-ACK	Antonov An-24B	Instructional airframe
CCCP-85010	Tupolev Tu-154	Instructional airframe
CCCP-85011	Tupolev Tu-154	Instructional airframe
CCCP-42311	Yakovlev Yak-42	Instructional airframe

Serbia

Belgrade

Belgrade Airport

| YU-AJM | Douglas DC-9-32 | Fuselage. Ground trainer. |

Museum of Aviation
Сурчин, P.O.Box 35, Beograd 11271, Serbia

7208	AAC-1 Toucan (Ju52)	Yugoslav Air Force
71214	Douglas C-47A	Yugoslav Air Force
YU-ABB	Douglas C-47A	JAT
71301	Ilyushin IL-14	Yugoslav Air Force
0662	Short SA.6 Sealand	Yugoslav Air Force
YU-AHB	Sud SE.210 Caravelle 6N	JAT

Slovakia

Banská Bystrica

Memorial and the Museum of the Slovak National Uprising (SNP)
Kapitulská 23, 974 01 Banska Bystrica, Slovakia
www.muzeumsnp.sk

2105	Lisunov Li-2 T	Marked '20 WHITE'. Fake Soviet Air Force markings.

Dubnica nad Vahom

Letecke Muzeum Slavnica
018 54 Sedmerovec, Slovakia

OM-VHB	Antonov An-2R	
5101	Avia AV-14 S(M)	Ex-Czechoslovak Air Force
OK-BYQ	Lisunov Li-2 T	Ex-Czechoslovak Government
OK-AFB	Tupolev Tu-134A	CSA Czechoslovak Airlines

Kosice

Muzeum Letectva Kosice
041 75 Kosice-Barca, Slovakia

CCCP-70271	Antonov An-2P	Ex-Aeroflot
3153	Avia AV-14T	Ex-Czechoslovak Air Force
HA-MOI	Ilyusin IL-18V	Malev
OM-BYO	Tupolev Tu-154M	Slovak Government
OM-BYE	Yakovlev Yak-40	Slovak Government

Malacky

Malacky Air Base
901 01 Malacky, Slovakia

5803	Antonov An-24	Slovak Air Force Stored, to be put on display.
0927	LET 410 UVP	Slovak Air Force Instructional airframe

Martin

Tomcany Aeroclub Museum
036 01 Martin, Slovakia

OM-RIQ	Antonov An-2	
OK-AND	LET 410A	Slov-Air

Nitra

Slovak Agricultural Museum
Dlha 92, Nitra 949 01, Slovakia

OM-JIE	Antonov An-2R	

Piešťany

Piešťany Airport Museum
Žilinská cesta 6545, Žilinská cesta 6545, 921 01 Piešťany, Slovakia

2506	Antonov An-26B	Slovak Air Force
1203	LET 410 FG	Slovak Air Force
0404	LET 410 MA	Slovak Air Force
0823	Yakovlev Yak-40	Slovak Government

Podnipliky

Restaurant Lietadlo
www.tajana.sk/lietadlo

3156	Avia AV-14 T	In use as a restaurant/bar

Svidnick

Military Museum and Memorial of the Soviet Army
Bardejovska 14, Svidnik 089 01, Slovakia

2107	Lisunov Li-2 T	Fake Soviet Air Force markings

Vysneho Kamarinka

| 2106 | Lisunov Li-2 T | Fake Soviet Air Force markings. By side of road west of village. |

Slovenia

Lesce-Bled

Lesce-Bled Airfield

S5-CAR	Antonov An-2	

Ljubljana

Ljubljana Airport

YU-AFF	Douglas DC-6B	Inex-Adria Airways

Otok

8332 Otok, Slovenia

71253	Douglas C-47A	Ex-Yugoslav Air Force Next to road north of the village.

Spain

Alcantarilla

Alcantarilla Air Base
Av. de Lorca, S/N, 30820 Alcantarilla, Murcia, Spain

T.12B-28	CASA 212	Spanish Air Force
T.2B-181	CASA 352L	Spanish Air Force

Barcelona

Parc Aeronautique de Catalunya
Sabadell Airport, Ctra. de Bellaterra, 08205 Sabadell, Barcelona, Spain

SP-ALG	Antonov An-2	
EC-ASP	Douglas C-47B	Spantax. Under restoration.

Fuenlabrada

CEFOIM Technical School
Calle Sauce, 28942 Fuenlabrada, Madrid, Spain
www.formacioncefoim.com

EC-EHC	Dassault Falcon 20	Instructional airframe
T.9-10	De Havilland Canada DHC-4 Caribou	Spanish Air Force Instructional airframe

University Rey Juan Carlos – Fuenlabrada Campus

Camino Del Molino S/N, 28943 Fuenlabrada, Madrid, Spain
www.urjc.es

EC-EDC	Dassault Falcon 20	Instructional airframe

Igualada

Igualada-Odena Aerodrome

08711, Barcelona, Spain

T.12B-16	CASA 212	Spanish Air Force

Las Palmas (Canary Islands)

Aerodromo de El Berriel

GC-500, 5X, 35107, Las Palmas, Spain

EC-BBT	Douglas DC-7C	Wears false Binter Canarias colours.

Gando Air Base (Las Palmas Airport)

T.12B-54	CASA 212	Spanish Air Force
T.12B-58	CASA 212	Spanish Air Force

Madrid

Barajas Airport

EC-BQZ	Douglas DC-9-32	Iberia Outside between terminals 1 and 2.

EC-EFH	Rockwell 690A Turbo Commander	Mounted on poles in roundabout at centre of airfield.

Cuatros Vientos Airfield

EC-ASJ	Beech C-45H	Based at FIO near Real Aero Club building. Airworthy.
T.9-29	De Havilland Canada DHC-4 Caribou	Spanish Air Force Mounted on poles. Inside base.
G-AEML	De Havilland DH.89 Dragon Rapide	Based at FIO near Real Aero Club building. Airworthy.

Cuatros Vientos Museo Del Aire
A-5, Km. 10,7, 28024 Madrid, Spain
www.ejercitodelaire.mde.es

TM.17-4	Boeing 707-351C	Spanish Air Force
EC-CFK	Boeing 727-256	Iberia Forward fuselage
TK.1-3	Boeing KC-97	Spanish Air Force
T.7-6	CASA 207 Azor	Spanish Air Force
T.7-17	CASA 207 Azor	Spanish Air Force
TR.12A-3	CASA 212	Spanish Air Force
XT.12-1	CASA 212	Spanish Air Force
T.2B-211	CASA 352L	Spanish Air Force
T.2B-254	CASA 352L	Spanish Air Force
T.9-25	De Havilland Canada DHC-4 Caribou	Spanish Air Force
EC-AKO	De Havilland DH.89 Dragon Rapide	
G-ACYR	De Havilland DH.89 Dragon Rapide	
T.3-36	Douglas C-47	Spanish Air Force

| T.4-10 | Douglas C-54A | Spanish Air Force. Cockpit |
| E.18-3 | Piper PA-31P | Spanish Air Force |

Getafe Air Base

T.7-1	CASA 207 Azor	Spanish Air Force
T.7-19	CASA 207 Azor	Spanish Air Force
T.12B-64	CASA 212	Spanish Air Force
T.4-8	Douglas C-54A	Spanish Air Force

Getafe Perales del Rio

| T.12B-56 | CASA 212 | Spanish Air Force. Mounted on poles in roundabout on Av. Alva Myrdal. |

Torrejon Air Base

| D.3B-7 | CASA 212 | |
| T.2B-246 | CASA 352L | Spanish Air Force |

Malaga

Museo de Aeropuertos y Transporte Aereo

Plaza Pierre George Latécoère, Avenida García Morato, 29004 Málaga, Spain
www.aeroplaza.org

N9886A	Beech 18	Wears false Spantax colours
N8042W	Convair CV-440	Wears false Kar-Air colours
N9888A	De Havilland DH.104 Dove	Marked PH-VLA

EC-ABC	Douglas C-47	Iberia Marked EC-CPO
EC-CGO	Douglas DC-9-32	Iberia Forward fuselage

Mallorca (Balearic Islands)

Globalia Formación
07609 Llucmajor, Balearic Islands, Spain

EC-DXG	Rockwell 680 Turbo Commander

Palma Airport

D-3B-6	CASA 212	Spanish Air Force
EC-BZO	Convair CV-990 Coronado	Spantax Poor condition

Son Bonet Airport
Edificio Antiguo Centro de Control, Ctra.Palma-Inca, km 6, 07141 Marratxí, Islas Baleares, Spain

ER-AJM	Antonov An-2
EC-EJB	Douglas C-47

Salamanca

Matacan Airport

T.12B-25	CASA 212	Spanish Air Force
EC-BUG	Douglas TC-47B	Spanish Air Force Marked T.3-59

| G-BHUA | Douglas C-47A | Spanish Air Force. Marked T.3-28. Mounted on poles. |

San Torcuato

Flight School San Torcuato
Camino de la Calzada, s/n, 26291 San Torcuato, La Rioja, Spain

| T.9-9 | De Havilland Canada DHC-4 Caribou | Spanish Air Force |

Seville

Seville Airport

| EC-FAD | CASA CN-235 | Wears false Airbus colours. Outside Airbus facility. |

Villanubla

Valladolid Airport Air Base
N-601, Km. 206, 47620 Villanubla, Valladolid, Spain

| T.12B-15 | CASA 212 | Spanish Air Force |
| T.9-23 | De Havilland Canada DHC-4 Caribou | Spanish Air Force |

Vilanova i la Geltru

EFAV – Escola de Formacio Aeronautica

Carrer de la Unió, 81, 08800 Vilanova i la Geltrú, Barcelona, Spain
www.efav.cat

XS729	British Aerospace Dominee T.1	Royal Air Force Instructional airframe

Sweden

Karlsborg

Karlsborg Fortress
Fortifikationsgatan 8B, 546 30 Karlsborg, Sweden

79002	Douglas C-47A	Swedish Air Force

Kulltorp

High Chaparral Wild West Theme Park
High Chaparral, 330 31 Kulltorp, Sweden
www.highchaparral.se

SE-IVY	Vickers Viscount 815	Mounted on poles. Damaged by fire, but still present.

Linköping

Air Force Museum
Carl Cederströms gata 2, 586 63 Linköping, Sweden
www.flygvapenmuseum.se

79007	Douglas C-47A	Swedish Air Force
79001	Douglas DC-3	Swedish Air Force. Wreckage.
86002	Rockwell Sabreliner 40	Swedish Air Force
83008	Percival Pembroke C52	Swedish Air Force

85172	Sud SE.210 Caravelle 3	Swedish Air Force
82001	Vickers Varsity T.1	Swedish Air Force

E4 Motorway Exit 113
582 74 Linköping, Sweden

SE-ISF	Saab 340A	Prototype. Mounted on poles.

Ljungbyhed

Flygteknikcenter
264 51 Ljungbyhed, Sweden

N12AM	Cessna 500 Citation I	Instructional airframe
G-JBIZ	Cessna 550F Citation II	Instructional airframe

Malmo

Teknikens Museum
Malmöhusvägen 7A, 211 18 Malmö, Sweden
www.malmo.se

SE-CNK	Vickers Viscount 784D	Cockpit

Norrtalje

Hotel Roslagen
Stockholmsvägen 53, 761 43 Norrtälje, Sweden
www.hotelroslagen.se

42-24049	Douglas DC-3	Wears false SAS Scandinavian Airlines colours.

Nyköping

Flygteknik Technical Training
General Schybergs väg 12, 611 92 Nyköping, Sweden

SE-002	Saab 2000	Prototype

Ostersund

Teknikland
OPTANDS FLYGFÄLT 106, 831 92 Östersund, Sweden
www.teknikland.se

CN-MAL	Beech 18D/S	Under restoration

Ostra Vemmerlov

Österlens Flygmuseum
ÖSTBO, VEMMERLÖV, 272 97 Gärsnäs, Sweden
www.osterlensflygmuseum.se

G-ANVU	De Havilland DH.104 Dove	Marked 46002. Under restoration.

Skurup

Stenbäcks Flygmuseum
Rockarpsvägen, 233 91 Svedala, Sweden
www.stenbacksflygmuseum.se

G-BTZH	British Aerospace ATP	Ex-West Air Europe. Cockpit.
SE-LID	Hawker Siddeley HS.748 2A	Ex-West Air Europe. Cockpit.

Stockholm

Arlanda Aircraft Museum
Kabinvägen 7, Stockholm–Arlanda

SE-EUR	De Havilland DH.104 Dove	Not on display
SE-BXU	Lockheed Electra L12A	
SE-BZE	Lockheed Lodestar	

Arlanda Airport

85210	Sud SE.210 Caravelle 3	Wears Le Caravelle Club titles. Marked SE-DAI.
SE-DAA	Sud SE.210 Caravelle 3	Ground trainer. Nose missing.
SE-DAF	Sud SE.210 Caravelle 3	SAS Scandinavian Airlines

Arlanda Eurostop Shopping Mall
Cederströms Slinga 80, 195 61 Arlandastad, Sweden

83004	Percival Pembroke C52	Hung from ceiling

Arlanda Jumbo Stay Hostel

Jumbovägen 4, 190 47 Stockholm-Arlanda, Sweden
www.jumbostay.com

N981JM	Boeing 747-212B	Used as a hotel

Bromma Airport

SE-CFP	Douglas C-47A	SAS Scandinavian Airlines. Airworthy.

Sundsvall

Car Park

6 Timmervägen, Birsta, Sundsvall, Västernorrland County

LY-AEH	Antonov An-2	

Ugglarp

Svedino's Automobile and Aircraft Museum

Ullarp 123, 311 69 Ugglarp, Sweden
www.svedinos.se

T.2B-142	Casa 352L	Marked DP+FJ 640416
OH-VKC	Douglas DC-3D	Ex-Kar-Air
83007	Percival Pembroke C52	Swedish Air Force

Västerås

Stockholm Västerås Airport

N428UE	British Aerospace Jetstream 31-01	Instructional airframe. Aviation College of Sweden

Switzerland

Basel

EuroAirport Basel-Mulhouse-Freiburg Airport

HB-IRJ	Douglas DC-3	Super Constellation Flyers Association Breitling titles. Airworthy
HB-ISH	Fokker F27-200	Ex-Sunshine Aviation Fuselage. Ground trainer.
HB-RSC	Lockheed C-121C Super Constellation	Super Constellation Flyers Association Breitling titles. Airworthy
G-AIVG	Vickers Viking 1B	Balair. Under restoration. www.save-a-viking.org titles

Dubendorf

Flieger Flab Museum
Überland Str. 255, 8600 Dübendorf, Switzerland
www.airforcecenter.ch

HB-GAC	Beech 18 C/S	
HB-HOY	CASA 352L	JU-Air Airworthy
HB-HOP	Junkers Ju-52 3m g4e	JU-Air Airworthy
HB-HOS	Junkers Ju-52 3m g4e	JU-Air Airworthy

| HB-HOT | Junkers Ju-52 3m g4e | JU-Air
Airworthy |

Geneva

Geneva Airport

| F-GCJL | Boeing 737-222 | Ex-Air Mediterranee
Ground trainer |

Grenchen

Grenchen Airport
Flughafenstrasse 117, 2540 Grenchen, Switzerland

| N431HM | Douglas DC-3 | Swissair
Airworthy |

Lucerne

Swiss Museum of Transport
Lidostrasse 5, 6006 Luzern, Switzerland
www.verkehrshaus.ch

HB-ICC	Convair CV-990 30-A6	Swissair Mounted on poles
HB-IRN	Douglas DC-3	Swissair Mounted on poles
HB-LBO	Fokker F.VIII	Swissair

Zürich

Runway 34 Restaurant

Rohrholzstrasse 67, 8152 Glattbrugg, Switzerland
www.runway34.ch

01146	Ilyushin IL-14T	Russian State Transport Company. Used as a restaurant.

Turkey

Ankara

Air Force Museum
Bahçekapı Mahallesi, 06990 Etimesgut/Ankara, Turkey
hvkk.tsk.tr

12-073/6073	Douglas C-47A	Turkish Air Force
69-039	VFW Transall C-160D	Turkish Air Force

Etimesgut Air Base

H-039	Douglas C-47A	Turkish Air Force

Çankir

Çankırı Recep Tayyip Erdoğan Parkı
Buğday Pazarı Mahallesi, Esentepe Cd. No:54, 18100 Çankırı Merkez/Çankırı,
Turkey

TC-ACC	Airbus A300B4-203F	Used as a library

Edremit

Ucak Restaurant
Kızıklı Mah., Büyük Kara Ağaç Sk., 10700 Çoruk Köyü/Burhaniye/Burhaniye/
Balıkesir, Turkey
www.korfezucakrestaurant.com

| TC-JDK | Airbus A340-311 | Used as a restaurant |

Erkilit

Erkilit Airport
Ahmet Yasevi Mahallesi, Mustafa Kemal Paşa Blv., 38090 Merkez/Kocasinan/
Kayseri, Turkey

| E-076 | Douglas DC-3 | Turkish Air Force |
| 61-0963 | Lockheed C-130B Hercules | Turkish Air Force |

Erzincan

Erzincan University
Fatih Mahallesi, Sivas Erzincan Yolu Yalnızbağ Yerleşkesi, 24100 Merkez/Erzin-
can, Turkey

| TC-MBF | Fokker F27-600 | Wears false THY colours. Instructional airframe. |

Eskisehir

Andolu University, Eskisehir Airport
Gazipaşa Mahallesi, 26555 Eskişehir Merkez/Eskişehir Province, Turkey

| TC-AUV | Beech C90 | Instructional airframe |

TC-SHA	Beech C90GTI	Instructional airframe
TC-SHB	Beech C90GTI	Instructional airframe
N269FE	Boeing 727-233F	Ex-FedEx Express. Instructional airframe.
431	Vickers Viscount 749D	Ex-Turkish Air Force. Instructional airframe.

Havacilik Museum
Yenibağlar Mahallesi, 26170 Tepebaşı/Eskişehir Province, Turkey
havacilikparki.anadolu.edu.tr

052/6032	Douglas C-47A	Turkish Air Force. Incorporated into small building.

Istanbul

Büyükçekmece
Fatih Mahallesi, Kordonboyu Cd., 34500 Büyükçekmece/İstanbul, Turkey

12-069/6069	Douglas C-47A	Turkish Air Force. Mounted on poles next to shore.

Istanbul Aviation Museum
Yeşilköy Mahallesi,, Eski Havaalanı Caddesi,, 34149 Bakırköy/İstanbul, Turkey
www.hdo.edu.tr

TC-ERK	De Havilland DH.89 Dragon Rapide	
H-008	Douglas DC-3	Turkish Air Force
YSL-52	Douglas DC-3	Turkish Air Force
ETI-683	Douglas C-54D	Turkish Air Force
TC-ABA	Sud SE.210 Caravelle 10R	Istanbul Airlines
69-022	VFW Transall C-160D	Turkish Air Force

| 430 | Vickers Viscount 749D | Turkish Air Force |

KidZania Istanbul

Acıbadem Mahallesi, Çeçen sok. No:25, 34660 Acıbadem/Üsküdar/Üsküdar/İstanbul, Turkey
www.kidzania.com.tr

| XA-UKW | Boeing 737-205 | Forward fuselage mounted next to KidZania entrance. |

Rahmi M. Koç Museum

Keçeci Piri Mahallesi, Rahmi M Koç Museum Hasköy Cad. No:5, 34445 Beyoğlu/İstanbul, Turkey
www.rmk-museum.org.tr

| TC-ALI | Douglas C-47A | Ex-Nexu Airlines. Mounted on poles. |
| TC-LEY | HFB 320 Hansa Jet | |

Izmir

Gaziemir Air Base

| E-062/6062 | Douglas C-47A | Turkish Air Force. Requires base access. |

Kastamonu

Kastamonu Ucak Restaurant

Aktekke Mahallesi, Arkayol Sk. No:10, 37200 Kastamonu Merkez/Kastamonu, Turkey

| TC-TUA | McDonnell Douglas MD-82 | Used as a restaurant |

Kavagi

Military Base
Poyraz Mahallesi, 34829 Beykoz/Istanbul, Turkey

H-011	Douglas C-47B	Turkish Air Force. Inaccessible without permission.

Konya

Türk Yildizlari Ucak Restaurant
Büyükkayacık Mahallesi, 42250 Büyükkayacık Osb/Selçuklu/Konya, Turkey
www.ucakkaferestaurant.com

TC-FLJ	Airbus A300B2K-3C	Used as a café/restaurant.

Kuthaya

Air Force Museum
Cumhuriyet Mahallesi, 43020 Kütahya Merkez/Kütahya, Turkey

12-003	Douglas C-47B	Turkish Air Force

Tekirdag

Uçak Restaurant Yurdanurlar Çiftlik tekirdağ
Değirmenaltı Mahallesi, İstanbul Blv. No:29, 59000 Süleymanpaşa/Tekirdağ, Turkey
www.yurdanurlarciftlik.com

TC-MNJ	Airbus A300B4-203	Used as a restaurant.

Ukraine

Berezan

North East of Town Centre
Berezan', Kyivs'ka oblast, Ukraine, 07540

UR-56386	Antonov An-2R	Mounted on concrete blocks

Chubinskoye

Kyivs'ka oblast, Ukraine

CCCP-67002	LET 410 UVP	Aeroflot Near paintball centre

Hostomel

Next to T1002 Road

CCCP-08828	Antonov An-2T	

Kalmiuske

Camp Site
Petrivs'ke, Петрівське, Donetsk Oblast, Ukraine 87221

CCCP-73951	Ilyushin IL-12	Aeroflot

Kharkiv

National Aerospace University
Kharkiv, Kharkiv Oblast, Ukraine, 61000

CCCP-67178	LET 410 UVP	Aeroflot

Sokolniki Factory
Sumska St, 134, Kharkiv, Харківська, Ukraine, 61000

47 Red	Tupolev Tu-104A	Soviet Air Force
CCCP-65655	Tupolev Tu-134A	Aeroflot Ukraine Marked UR-65713

Kiev

Borispol Airport

UR-85407	Tupolev Tu-154 B2	Ex-Avialini Ground trainer

Faculty of Aviation and Space Systems
Botkina St, 1, Kyiv, Ukraine, 03056

02 Blue	Antonov An-24T	Ex-Ukraine Navy Fuselage

National Aviation University
Kosmonavta Komarova Ave, 1, Kyiv, Ukraine, 02000

UR-46713	Antonov An-24	Ex-Aeroflot Instructional airframe
UR-26194	Antonov An-26	
CCCP-67250	LET 410 M	Ex-Aeroflot Instructional airframe

UR-85009	Tupolev Tu-154	Ex-Aeroflot Instructional airframe
CCCP-87683	Yakovlev Yak-40	Ex-Aeroflot
CCCP-42303	Yakovlev Yak-42	Instructional airframe

National Technical University of Ukraine
просп. Перемоги, 37, Kyiv, Ukraine, 03056
www.kpi.ua

| UR-87685 | Yakovlev Yak-40 | Ex-Air Ukraine |

Patrol Police Department National Headquarters
9, Kyiv, Ukraine, 02000

| UR-49252 | Antonov An-24B | Ex-Air Ukraine Instructional trainer. 1 mile north of Zhulyany Airport. |

Ukrainian State Museum of the Great Patriotic War
Lavrska vul. 24, Kiev 01015, Ukraine
warmuseum.kiev.ua

| 54 Red | Lisunov Li-2 | Soviet Air Force |

Zhulyany Airport

| UR-47287 | Antonov An-24B | Painted to promote 2017 Eurovision Song Contest. Outside terminal. |

Zhulyany Aviation Museum
Vulytsya Medova, 1, Kyiv, Ukraine, 02000
www.aviamuseum.com.ua

UR-54812	Antonov An-2	
14 Red	Antonov An-2T	Ukraine Air Force
UR-ANC	Antonov An-2T	
UR-49256	Antonov An-24T	Ukraine Air Force
CCCP-46245	Antonov An-24B	Aeroflot
UR-46569	Antonov An-24B	Marked UR-46801
22 Blue	Antonov An-26	Ukraine Air Force
UR-26215	Antonov An-26	Uhuru Airlines To be used as a restaurant
UR-30005	Antonov An-30	Ukraine Airlines
CCCP-780361	Antonov An-71	Antonov Design Bureau Aeroflot colours
CCCP-52036	Avia AV-14 P	Aeroflot
CCCP-75634	Ilyushin IL-18A	Aeroflot
CCCP-86696	Ilyushin IL-62	Aeroflot
CCCP-76511	Ilyushin IL-76T	Aeroflot
CCCP-86000	Ilyushin IL-86	Aeroflot
CCCP-67357	LET 410 UVP	Aeroflot
CCCP-L5415	Tupolev Tu-104 G	Aeroflot
CCCP-45092	Tupolev Tu-124	Aeroflot
CCCP-65601	Tupolev Tu-134	Aeroflot In poor condition
43 Blue	Tupolev Tu-134 UBL	Ukraine Air Force
CCCP-65743	Tupolev Tu-134 A	Aeroflot
CCCP-65782	Tupolev Tu-134 A-3	Ukraine Government
CCCP-85020	Tupolev Tu-154	Aeroflot
UR-MHG	Yakovlev Yak-40	

UR–XYZ	Yakovlev Yak–40	
UR–SAN	Yakovlev Yak–40	Globus
UR–87479	Yakovlev Yak–40	To be moved to Glehva?

Kirovgrad

Flight Academy Museum

Oleksandrivs'ke Shose, 53, Kirovohrad, Kirovohrads'ka oblast, Ukraine, 25000

CCCP–47816	Antonov An–24 RV	Aeroflot
UR–67417	LET 410 UVP	Ukraine Flight State Academy. Mounted on metal frame.
UR–87832	Yakovlev Yak–40	Ex–Donbassaero

Koktobel

Blue Lagoon Centre

Lenina St, 120, Koktebel', Crimea, 98186

CCCP–46793	Antonov An–24B	Ex–Aeroflot

Kryviyi Rih

Aviation Museum

50000, ulitsa Kuprina, 132, Kryvyi Rih, Dnipropetrovsk Oblast, Ukraine, 50000

CCCP–11344	Antonov An–12B	Aeroflot
CCCP–47754	Antonov An–24B	Aeroflot
CCCP–26575	Antonov An–26	Aeroflot
CCCP–65615	Tupolev Tu–134	Aeroflot
CCCP–85040	Tupolev Tu–154B	Aeroflot

CCCP-85131	Tupolev Tu-154B	Aeroflot
CCCP-85149	Tupolev Tu-154B	Aeroflot
CCCP-76485	Tupolev Tu-114B	Aeroflot
CCCP-87766	Yakovlev Yak-40	Aeroflot
CCCP-87733	Yakovlev Yak-40	Aeroflot
CCCP-42533	Yakovlev Yak-42	Aeroflot

Technical College
Kuprina St, 129, Kryvyi Rih, Дніпропетровська, Ukraine, 50000

| CCCP-87734 | Yakovlev Yak-40 | Ex-Aeroflot Ukraine |

Luhansk

Aviation Museum
Luhansk, Luhans'ka oblast, Ukraine, 91000

UR-40829	Antonov An-2R	Fuselage
UR-46514	Antonov An-24RV	AeroSvit
41 Red	Antonov An-26Sh	Ukraine Air Force
CCCP-73975	Ilyushin IL-12	Aeroflot
10 Red	Ilyushin IL-38	Soviet Navy
CCCP-76621	Ilyushin IL-76 MD	Soviet Air Force
50 Black	Tupolev Tu-124Sh	Soviet Air Force
CCCP-87345	Yakovlev Yak-40	SanAir

Lutsk

City Centre
Lutsk, Volyns'ka oblast, Ukraine, 43000

CCCP-75659	Ilyushin IL-18B	Aeroflot

Nikolayev

Zatyshnyy Dvoryk Café
18A, Budivelnykiv St, 18A, Mykolaiv, Mykolaivs'ka oblast, Ukraine, 54000

CCCP-75844	Ilyushin IL-18 V	Aeroflot

Odessa

Military Academy
Fontans'ka Road, 10, Odesa, Odessa Oblast, Ukraine, 65000

10 White	Antonov An-2	Ukraine Air Force Instructional airframe

Poltava

Museum of Long Range Aviation
вул. Олександра Засядька 1, Poltava, Poltavs'ka oblast, Ukraine, 36000
www.mvba.com.ua

42 Blue	Tupolev Tu-134 UBL	Ukraine Air Force

MVS Training Centre

Viktora Nosova Ln, 31-27, Poltava, Poltavs'ka oblast, Ukraine 36000

| UR-67198 | LET 410 UVP | Ex-Air Ukraine. Mounted on concrete blocks. |

Rokytne

East of Town Centre

Entuziastiv Vul., Rokytne, Kyivs'ka oblast, Ukraine 09600

| UR-LUX | Yakovlev Yak-40 | |

Slavyansk

Technical School

Aerodromna Vulytsya, Slavyansk, Donetsk Oblast, Ukraine

CCCP-11351	Antonov An-12B	Ex-Aeroflot Instructional airframe
CCCP-46684	Antonov An-24RV	Ex-Aeroflot Instructional airframe
CCCP-46762	Antonov An-24	Ex-Aeroflot Instructional airframe
CCCP-87721	Yakovlev Yak-40	Ex-Aeroflot Mounted on poles near entrance
CCCP-87720	Yakovlev Yak-40	Ex-Aeroflot

Tarasivka

Town Centre
Shevchenka Street, Tarasivka, Kyivs'ka oblast, Ukraine 08161

UR-87591	Yakovlev Yak-40K		Ex-UES-Avia

Vasilkov

Vasilkovsky College National Aviation University
Dekabrystiv St, 37, Vasylkiv, Kyivs'ka oblast, Ukraine, 08602
vik.nau.edu.ua

UR-87964	Yakovlev Yak-40		Ex-Ukraine Government. Instructional airframe.

Vyshhorod

Coordinates: 50.59036636N 30.42556190E

39 Red	Antonov An-26		Ex-Ukraine Air Force

Yevpatoria

Outside military base
Yevpatoriya 97400

70 Red	Ilyushin IL-14		Soviet Air Force. Mounted on concrete blocks.

Zaporozhye

Technical Museum Bohuslayeva

Kopenkina St, 27A, Zaporizhzhia, Zaporiz'ka oblast, Ukraine, 69000
museum.motorsich.com

Unknown	Antonov An-2	Motor Sich
		Mounted on pole

Zhytomyr

Yuri Gagarin Park of Culture and Rest

вул. Старий Бульвар, 34, Zhytomyr, Zhytomyrs'ka oblast, Ukraine, 10000

CCCP-42387	Tupolev Tu-104A	Aeroflot
		In poor condition

United Kingdom

Alton

The Departure Lounge Café
Basingstoke Rd, Alton GU34 4BH
www.thedepartureloungecafe.co.uk

G-AWYV	BAC 1-11-501EX	Forward fuselage. Used as a café.

Balcombe

Wings Museum
Unit 1, Bucklands Farm, Brantridge Lane, Balcombe RH17 6JT
www.wingsmuseum.co.uk

K-1	Douglas C-47A	Fuselage. Ex-Belgian Air Force. In poor condition.
51-2700	Fairchild C119G Packet	Cockpit

Bedford

Bedford College
Cauldwell St, Bedford MK42 9AH
www.bedford.ac.uk

XX495	Handley Page Jetstream T.1	Instructional airframe. Ex-Royal Air Force.

Belfast

Ulster Folk and Transport Museum
Cultra, 153 Bangor Rd, Holywood, Northern Ireland, BT18 0EU
www.nmni.com

G-BKMW	Short SD3-30-100	Cockpit

Birmingham

Solihull College
Woodlands Campus, Auckland Dr, Solihull B36 0NF
www.solihull.ac.uk

XX478	Handley Page Jetstream T.2	Instructional airframe

Bolton

Steaks on a Plane
Chamberlain St, Bolton BL3
www.steakhouseco.com

VP-BRU	Boeing 737-528	Forward fuselage. Used as a restaurant.

Bournemouth

Bournemouth Aviation Museum
B3073, Merritown Lane, Hurn, Christchurch BH23 6BA
www.aviation-museum.co.uk

G-ISLG	ATR 42-310	Fuselage. Often relocated to beach in summer.

ZE432	BAC 1-11-479FU	Forward fuselage. QinetiQ ETPS markings.
G-CEAH	Boeing 737-229	Forward fuselage. Palmair titles.
G-BEYF	Handley Page HPR-7 Herald 401	Cockpit
ZD620	HS/BAe 125 CC.3	Fuselage. Ex-Royal Air Force.
G-BKRL	Miles Leopard	
G-OPAS	Vickers Viscount 806	Cockpit. Parcel Force colours.

Brenzett

Brenzett Aeronautical Museum
Ivychurch Rd, Brenzett, Romney Marsh, Kent, TN29 0EE
www.rmwcollection.co.uk

G-AMSM	Douglas C-47A	Cockpit

Bristol

Aerospace Bristol
Hayes Way, Patchway, Bristol BS34 5BZ
www.aerospacebristol.org

G-BOAF	Aerospatiale/BAC Concorde 102	British Airways. Last Concorde to fly.
G-ALRX	Bristol Britannia 101	Forward fuselage.
NZ5911	Bristol Type 170 Freighter	Under restoration

Brize Norton

RAF Brize Norton
Carterton, Oxfordshire, OX18 3LX

KN566	Douglas C-47B	Royal Air Force

Bruntingthorpe

Cold War Jets Collection
Bruntingthorpe Proving Ground, Lutterworth, Leicestershire, LE17 5QS
www.bruntingthorpeaviation.com

F-BTGV	Aero Spacelines 377 Guppy	Ex-Airbus Industrie
SX-OAD	Boeing 747-212B	Olympic Airways
G-CPDA	De Havilland DH106 Comet 4C	Royal Aircraft Establishment. Performs ground runs.
XX494	Handley Page Jetstream T1	Royal Air Force
XV226	Hawker Siddeley Nimrod MR.2P	Royal Air Force. Performs ground runs.
ZD241	Vickers VC10 K.4	Royal Air Force. Performs ground runs.
ZA147	Vickers Super VC10 K.3	Royal Air Force. Performed last ever VC10 flight.

Cambridge

Imperial War Museum Duxford
Duxford, Cambridge CB22 4QR
www.iwm.org.uk

G-AXDN	Aerospatiale/BAC Concorde 100	Prototype

G-ALZO	Airspeed Ambassador AS.57	Dan-Air London
G-ANTK	Avro York C.1	Dan-Air London
G-AVMU	BAC 1-11-510ED	British Airways
G-AOVT	Bristol Britannia 317	Monarch Airlines
G-BEVT	Britten Norman BN-2A Mk 111 Trislander	Aurigny Air Service
G-ALFU	De Havilland DH104 Dove 6	Civil Aviation Authority
G-BHUB	Douglas C-47A	Wears US Air Force colours. Marked 43-15509.
TG528	Handley Page Hastings C.1A	Royal Air Force
G-APWJ	Handley Page HPR-7 Herald 201	Air UK
G-ALDG	Handley Page Hermes IVA	Fuselage. BOAC.
G-AVFB	Hawker Siddeley HS.121 Trident 2E	British European Airways
ML796	Short Sunderland Mk5	Royal Air Force
G-ALWF	Vickers Viscount 701	British European Airways
G-ASGC	Vickers VC10 1151	BOAC

TWI Ltd
Granta Vale, Great Abington, Cambridge CB21 6AL
www.twi-global.com

N504EA	Eclipse EA500	Prototype. Preserved on roundabout.

Cardiff

International Centre for Aerospace Training
Cardiff Airport Business Park, Cardiff Airport, Rhoose, Barry CF62 3DP
www.cavc.ac.uk

D-AGEG	Boeing 737-35B	Forward fuselage. Instructional airframe.

XX487	Handley Page Jetstream T.2	Instructional airframe.

Cardiff Airport

G-AVMT	BAC 1-11-510ED	Fuselage. Ground trainer.

Carlisle

Solway Aviation Museum
Carlisle Airport, Crosby on Eden CA6 4NW
www.solway-aviation-museum-co.uk

XV259	Hawker Siddeley Nimrod AEW.3	Cockpit
G-ARPP	Hawker Siddeley HS.121 Trident 1C	Cockpit
WP314	Percival Sea Prince T.1	Royal Navy

Carluke

Reynard Nursery
Reynard, Carluke ML8 5HW
www.reynardnursery.co.uk

G-CONV	Convair CV-440	Ex-Air Atlantique

Chichester

Chichester College
Westgate Fields, Chichester PO19 1SB
www.chichester.ac.uk

F-GCSL	Boeing 737-222	Forward fuselage. Instructional airframe.

Colchester

Merville Barracks
Circular Rd S, Colchester CO2 7UT

KP208	Douglas C-47B	Royal Air Force. Marked KG374.

Cosford

Royal Air Force Museum
Lysander Ave, Cosford, Shifnal TF11 8UP
www.rafmuseum.org.uk/cosford

G-AGNV	Avro York C.1	Marked TS798
XP411	AW Argosy T.1	Royal Air Force
G-AOVF	Bristol Britannia 312	Wears false Royal Air Force colours. Marked XM497.
T.2B-272	CASA 352L	Wears false British Airways colours. Marked G-AFAP.
VP952	De Havilland DH104 Devon C2	Royal Air Force
G-APAS	De Havilland DH106 Comet 1XB	Wears false BOAC colours.
KN645	Douglas C-47B	Royal Air Force
TG511	Handley Page Hastings T.5	Royal Air Force
XX496	Handley Page Jetstream T.1	Royal Air Force
XV249	Hawker Siddeley Nimrod R.1P	Royal Air Force
XS705	Hawker Siddeley HS.125 Dominie T.1	Royal Air Force
XS639	Hawker Siddeley HS.748 Andover E3A	Royal Air Force
XV202	Lockheed C-130K Hercules C.3P	Royal Air Force
L-866	PBY-6A Catalina	Royal Danish Air Force
WV746	Percival Pembroke C.1	Royal Air Force

XL993	SA Twin Pioneer CC.1	Royal Air Force
XR371	Short Belfast C.1	Royal Air Force
WL679	Vickers Varsity T.1	Royal Air Force
XR808	Vickers VC10 C.1K	Royal Air Force

Coventry

Nimrod XV232

Coventry Airport, Baginton, Coventry CV8 3AZ
www.xv232.com

XV232	Hawker Siddeley Nimrod MR.2P	Royal Air Force

Midland Air Museum

Coventry Airport, Rowley Rd, Baginton CV3 4FR
www.midlandairmuseum.co.uk

G-APRL	AW Argosy 101	ELAN Cargo
G-ALCU	De Havilland DH104 Dove 2	Marked G-ALVD
G-ARYB	Hawker Siddeley HS.125 1	
G-CHNX	Lockheed L-188A Electra	Cockpit
G-BRNM	Miles Leopard	
F-BGNR	Vickers Viscount 708	Air Inter

The DC-6 Diner

Coventry Airport West, Coventry Rd, Baginton, Coventry CV8 3AZ
www.dc6diner.com

G-SIXC	Douglas DC-6A/B	Ex-Air Atlantique. Used as a restaurant.

Cranfield

Cranfield University
College Rd, Bedford MK43 0AL
www.cranfield.ac.uk

G-DOCB	Boeing 737-436	Instructional airframe
SP-KWN	British Aerospace Jetstream 3212	Instructional airframe
G-RAVL	Hawker Siddeley Jetstream 1	Instructional airframe

Cranwell

RAF Cranwell
Cranwell Village, Sleaford NG34 8HB

XS727	Hawker Siddeley HS.125 Dominie T.1	Royal Air Force. Gate guard.

Croydon

Croydon Airport Visitor Centre
Airport House, Purley Way, Croydon CR0 0XZ
www.croydonairport.org.uk

G-ANUO	De Havilland DH114 Heron 2C/D	Mounted on poles. Marked G-AOXL.

Darlington

International Fire Training Centre
Durham Tees Valley Airport, Darlington DL2 1LU

UR-UTA	ATR 42-320	Fuselage. Ground trainer.

G-AWZS	Hawker Siddeley HS.121 Trident 3B	Ground trainer. Ex-British Airways.
G-BKIE	Short SD3-30	Fuselage. Ground trainer. Marked G-JON.
G-AZNC	Vickers Viscount 813	Fuselage. Ground trainer.

Doncaster

Doncaster Sheffield Airport
Finningley, Doncaster DN9 3GE

| EC-DDX | Boeing 727-256 | Forward fuselage. Instructional airframe inside Directions hangar. |

South Yorkshire Aircraft Museum
Dakota Way, Lakeside, Doncaster DN4 7NW
www.southyorkshireaircraftmuseum.org.uk

XL149	Blackburn Beverley C.1	Cockpit
G-ARHX	De Havilland DH104 Dove 8	Being rebuilt
N4565L	Douglas DC-3	Fuselage
XX477	Handley Page Jetstream T.1	Fuselage. Ex-Royal Air Force.
G-ATXH	Handley Page Jetstream 200	Cockpit
XW666	Hawker Siddeley Nimrod R.1P	Cockpit. Damaged by crash.
G-BOCB	Hawker Siddeley HS.125 1B	Cockpit
G-OPFW	Hawker Siddeley HS.748 2A	Cockpit. Parcel Force.
WJ903	Vickers Varsity T.1	Cockpit
WJ476	Vickers Valetta T.3	Cockpit

Dumfries

Dumfries and Galloway Aviation Museum

Tinwald Downs Rd, Heathhall Industiral Estate, Dumfries DG1 3PH

www.dumfriesaviationmuseum.com

| XX483 | Handley Page Jetstream T.2 | Cockpit |
| G–AWZJ | Hawker Siddeley HS.121 Trident 3B | Forward fuselage. Ex–British Airways. |

Dunsfold

Aces High Ltd

59 Stovolds Hill, Cranleigh GU6 8TB

www.aviationfilming.com

N88892	Boeing 747–236B	Used as film prop.
N437UH	British Aerospace Jetstream 31	Fuselage. Used as film prop.
N437TH	British Aerospace Jetstream 31	Used as film prop
N881AA	Raytheon Premier I	Used as film prop

Dunsfold Airfield

| ZA150 | Vickers Super VC10 K.3 | Royal Air Force. Performs ground runs. |

East Fortune

National Museum of Flight Scotland

East Fortune Airfield, B1347, North Berwick EH39 5LF

www.nms.ac.uk

| G–BOAA | Aerospatiale/BAC Concorde 102 | British Airways |

G-AVMO	BAC 1-11-510ED	British Airways
G-JSSD	British Aerospace Jetstream 31	Prototype
G-ASUG	Beech 18E/S	Loganair
G-APFJ	Boeing 707-436	Forward fuselage. BOAC.
VH-SNB	De Havilland DH84A Dragon	
G-ANOV	De Havilland DH104 Dove 6	Civil Aviation Authority
N14234 G-ARPH Hawker Siddeley HS.121 Trident 1C Cockpit	Handley Page Jetstream 1	Fuselage
XV241	Hawker Siddeley Nimrod MR.2	Cockpit
G-AMOG	Vickers Viscount 807	British Airways

East Midlands

East Midlands Aeropark
Hill Top, Castle Donington, Derby DE74 2PS
www.eastmidlandsaeropark.org

G-BEOZ	AW Argosy 101	ELAN Cargo
G-ANUW	De Havilland DH.104 Dove 6	
XW664	Hawker Siddeley Nimrod R.1P	Royal Air Force
G-APES	Vickers Vanguard 953	Cockpit
G-BHDD	Vickers Varsity T.1	Royal Air Force
G-CSZB	Vickers Viscount 807	Cockpit
XV108	Vickers VC10 C.1K	Forward fuselage. Ex-Royal Air Force.

Farnborough

Farnborough Air Sciences Trust Museum

85 Farnborough Rd, Farnborough GU14 6TF
www.airsciences.org.uk

G-AWZI	Hawker Siddeley HS.121 Trident 3B	Cockpit

Fishburn

Fishburn Airfield

Garmondsway, Bishop Middleham, Co Durham DL17 9DY

D-IFSB	De Havilland DH104 Dove 6	

Flixton

Norfolk & Suffolk Aviation Museum

The Street, Flixton, Bungay NR35 1NZ
www.aviationmuseum.net

G-BDVS	Fokker F27-200	Cockpit. Ex-Air UK.
WF128	Percival Sea Prince T.1	Royal Navy
VX580	Vickers Valetta C.2	Royal Air Force

Glasgow

The Experience

Hillington Park, Montrose Avenue, Glasgow G52 4JR
www.theexperience.org.uk

VP-BRV	Boeing 737-528	Forward fuselage

Gloucester

Jet Age Museum

Meteor Business Park, Cheltenham Rd E, Gloucester GL2 9QL
www.jetagemuseum.org

| G–AWZU | Hawker Siddeley HS.121 Trident 3B | Forward fuselage |

Halesworth

Former Airfield

Unit 6B The Old Airfield Upper Holton, Hatchett Pl, Halesworth IP19 8NH

| CF–EPV | ATL.98 Carvair | Cockpit. In car park next to road. |

Hull

Fort Paull Museum

Battery Rd, Paull, Hull HU12 8FP
www.fortpaull.com

| XB259 | Blackburn Beverley C.1 | Royal Air Force |

Humberside Airport

| G–AVMP | BAC 1–11–510ED | Forward fuselage. Ground trainer. |

Inverness

Highland Aviation Museum
9 Dalcross Industrial Estate, By Inverness Airport, Dalcross Industrial Estate, Inverness IV2 7XB

G-ASVO	Handley Page HPR-7 Herald 213	Forward fuselage. Ex-Channel Express.
XV294	Hawker Siddeley Nimrod MR.2P	Forward fuselage.

Isle of Man

Manx Aviation and Military Museum
Ronaldsway Airport, IM9 2AT
www.maps.org.im

G-BGYT	Embraer 110P1 Bandeirante	Wears false Manx colours

Kemble

Cotswold Airport
Kemble Enterprise Pk, Cirencester GL7 6BA

N389DF	Boeing 737-3M8	Ground trainer. Ex-KD Avia.
G-MKGA	Boeing 747-2R7F	Used for events
EL-WXA	Bristol Britannia 253	Royal Air Force colours. Marked XM496. Flew last ever Britannia flight. See www.xm496.com
N19UG	Hawker Siddeley HS.125 Dominie T.1	Instructional airframe.
N19CU	Hawker Siddeley HS.125 Dominie T.1	Instructional airframe.
D-ADSB	VFW-Fokker 614	Instructional airframe.

Kendal

The Outdoor Adventure Company
Old Hutton, Kendal LA8 0NB
www.theoutdooradventurecompany.co.uk

TC-MBE	Fokker F27-500	Ex-MNG Airlines

Kettering

Tresham College
Windmill Ave, Kettering NN15 6ER
www.tresham.ac.uk

G-AVMJ	BAC 1-11-510ED	Forward fuselage. Instructional airframe.

Lisburn

Ulster Aviation Society
Gate 3, Maze Long Kesh, 94-b Halftown Road, Lisburn BT27 5RF
www.ulsteraviationsociety.org

VP957	De Havilland DH104 Devon C2	Cockpit
WF122	Percival Sea Prince T.1	Royal Navy
G-BDBS	Short SD3-30 UTT	

Liverpool

Speke Aerodrome Heritage Group
Liverpool Airport, Speke Aerodrome, Liverpool L24 8QD
www.spekeaero.org

G-JMAC	British Aerospace Jetstream 41	British Aerospace

G-ANCF	Bristol Britannia 308	
G-BEJD	Hawker Siddeley HS.748 1	Dan-Air London
G-ORAL	Hawker Siddeley HS.748 2A	Cockpit
G-SSWM	Short SD3-60-100	Cockpit

London

Brooklands Museum
Brooklands Rd, Weybridge KT13 0SL
www.brooklandsmuseum.com

G-BBDG	Aerospatiale/BAC Concorde 100	British Airways
G-ASYD	BAC 1-11-670	
XX499	Handley Page Jetstream T.1	Royal Air Force
G-APEJ	Vickers Vanguard 953	Cockpit
G-APEP	Vickers Vanguard 953	Hunting Cargo
WF372	Vickers Varsity T.1	Royal Air Force
G-AGRU	Vickers Viking 1	
G-APIM	Vickers Viscount 806	British Air Ferries
G-AZLP	Vickers Viscount 813	Cockpit
XT575	Vickers Viscount 837	Cockpit
A40-AB	Vickers VC10 1106	Government of Oman
G-ARVM	Vickers VC10 1101	Fuselage. Ex-British Airways.

Heathrow Airport

G-BOAB	Aerospatiale/BAC Concorde 102	British Airways. Parked at BA maintenance area.

KidZania London
Westfield London Shopping Centre, Ariel Way, White City, London W12 7GA
www.kidzania.co.uk

EI-DFA	Airbus A319-111	Forward fuselage. Wears false British Airways colours.

RAF Museum Hendon
Grahame Park Way, London NW9 5LL
www.rafmuseum.org.uk

N9050T	Douglas C-47A	Cockpit
G-BEOX	Lockheed Hudson IIIa	Royal Australian Air Force. Marked A16-199.
ML824	Short Sunderland Mk5	Royal Air Force

RAF Northolt
W End Rd, Ruislip HA4 6NG

ZD621	Hawker Siddeley HS.125 CC.3	Royal Air Force. Gate guard.

Science Museum
Exhibition Rd, Kensington, London SW7 2DD
www.sciencemuseum.org.uk

KN448	Douglas C-47B	Cockpit
G-ASSM	Hawker Siddeley HS.125 1	
G-LIOA	Lockheed 10A Electra	

London Colney

The de Havilland Aircraft Museum
Salisbury Hall, Shenley, London Colney AL2 1BU
www.dehavillandmuseum.co.uk

G-JEAO	British Aerospace BAe 146-100	Fuselage
G-AOJT	De Havilland DH106 Comet 1A	Fuselage. Air France.
G-AREA	De Havilland DH104 Dove 8	British Aerospace
G-AOTI	De Havilland DH114 Heron 2D	Rolls-Royce
G-AVFH	Hawker Siddeley HS.121 Trident 2E	Forward fuselage. British European Airways.
G-ARYC	Hawker Siddeley HS.125 1	Bristol Siddeley

London Gatwick

Gatwick Aviation Museum
Vallance By-Ways, Lowfield Heath Rd, Charlwood, Gatwick RH6 0BT
www.gatwick-aviation-museum.co.uk

G-GACA	Percival Sea Prince T.1	Royal Navy

Luton

London Luton Airport

VP-BJW	Boeing 737-301	Forward fuselage. Ground trainer. Next to car park.
G-AOVS	Bristol Britannia 175	Ground trainer. Ex-Redcoat Air Cargo. Fire dump.

Macclesfield

Macclesfield College

Park Ln, Macclesfield SK11 8LF
www.macclesfield.ac.uk

| G-BLKP | British Aerospace Jetstream 31 | Instructional airframe |

Manchester

Manchester Airport Runway Visitor Park

Wilmslow Old Rd, Ringway, Altrincham WA15 8XQ
www.manchesterairport.co.uk

G-BOAC	Aerospatiale/BAC Concorde 102	British Airways
G-IRJX	British Aerospace RJX100	British Aerospace. Prototype.
XV231	Hawker Siddeley Nimrod MR.2P	Royal Air Force
G-AWZK	Hawker Siddeley HS.121 Trident 3B	British European Airways
G-DMCA	McDonnell Douglas DC-10-30	Forward fuselage. Ex-Monarch Airlines.

Museum of Science and Industry

Liverpool Rd, Manchester M3 4FP
www.msimanchester.org.uk

| G-AWZP | Hawker Siddeley HS.121 Trident 3B | Cockpit |

Metheringham

Metheringham Airfield Visitor Centre

Westmoor Farm, Martin Moor, Metheringham, Lincoln, Lincolnshire LN4 3WF

| G-AMHJ | Douglas C-47A | Royal Air Force. Marked KG651. |

Newark

Newark Air Museum

The Showground, Drove Ln, Winthorpe, Coddington, Newark NG24 2NY
www.newarkairmuseum.org

XN819	AW Argosy C.1	Cockpit
XB261	Blackburn Beverley C.1	Cockpit
G-ARHI	De Havilland DH104 Dove 1B	
G-ANXB	De Havilland DH114 Heron 1B	British European Airways
TG517	Handley Page Hastings T.5	Royal Air Force
XX492	Handley Page Jetstream T.1	Royal Air Force
XS726	Hawker Siddeley HS.125 Dominie T.1	Royal Air Force
WF369	Vickers Varsity T.1	Royal Air Force

Newcastle Upon Tyne

Newcastle Aviation Academy

Newcastle International Airport, Woolsington NE13 8BT
www.ncl-coll.ac.uk

G-AZMF	BAC 1-11-530FX	Forward fuselage. Ex-European Aviation. Instructional airframe.
G-31-983	British Aerospace Jetstream 32	Fuselage. Instructional airframe.
C-GWJO	Boeing 737-2A3	Ex-WestJet. Instructional airframe.
G-BBYM	Handley Page Jetstream 200	Instructional airframe.

Newquay

Cornwall Aviation Heritage Centre
HAS 3 Aerohub Newquay, Saint Mawgan, Newquay TR8 4GP
www.cornwallaviationhc.co.uk

ZH763	BAC 1-11 539GL	QinetiQ
ZA148	Vickers VC10 K3	Royal Air Force

North Weald

North Weald Airfield
Merlin Way, North Weald CM16 6HR

N44914	Douglas C-54Q	US Air Force. Used as film prop.

Norwich

City of Norwich Aviation Museum
Old Norwich Rd, Horsham St Faith, Norwich NR10 3JF
www.cnam.org.uk

G-BHMY	Fokker F27-600	Air UK
G-ASKK	Handley Page HPR-7 Herald 201	Air UK
XV255	Hawker Siddeley Nimrod MR.2P	Royal Air Force

KLM Academy
5 Anson Rd, Norwich NR6 6ED

G-CELS	Boeing 737-377	Instructional airframe. Ex-Jet2

Nottingham

St John The Baptist Primary School
Vale Rd, Colwick, Nottingham NG4 2ED

G-SSWO	Short SD3-60-100	Used as a classroom

Old Sarum

Hangar 1, Old Sarum Airfield, Old Sarum, Salisbury SP4 6DZ
www.boscombedownaviationcollection.co.uk

XX919	BAC 1-11-402AP	Cockpit
G-PLAH	British Aerospace Jetstream 31	Cockpit
XK699	De Havilland DH106 Comet C.2	Forward fuselage. Ex-Royal Air Force.
XS790	Hawker Siddeley HS.748 CC.2	Cockpit

Perth

Air Service Training
Hangar 4, Perth Airport, Perth PH2 6PL
www.airservicetraining.co.uk

G-NFLC	Handley Page Jetstream 1	Instructional airframe

Pontypridd

University of South Wales
Lower Glyntaf, Pontypridd CF37 4BE
www.southwales.ac.uk

G-JXTC	British Aerospace Jetstream 31	Instructional airframe

Poole

Private Garden
Verity Crescent, Poole, Dorset BH17 8UA

G–BGNG	Short SD3-30-200	Forward fuselage

Prestwick

Glasgow Prestwick Airport

G–CELR	Boeing 737-330	Fuselage. Instructional airframe.

Ramsgate

RAF Manston History Museum
821 Manston Rd, Ramsgate CT12
www.rafmanston.co.uk

G–SSWP	Short SD3-30-100	Cockpit

Reading

Museum of Berkshire Aviation
Mohawk Way, Woodley, Reading RG5 4UE
www.museumofberkshireaviation.co.uk

G–APWA	Handley Page HPR-7 Herald 100	British European Airways. Prototype.
G–AMEW	Miles Marathon	Fuselage section.

Redberth

Apple Camping
Norchard Farmhouse, Redberth, Wales, SA70 8RX
www.applecamping.co.uk

N25AG	Lockheed Jetstar 2	Fuselage minus tail.

Shoreham

Northbrook College
Littlehampton Rd, Worthing BN12 6NU
www.northbrook.ac.uk

XX475	Handley Page Jetstream T.2	Instructional airframe
XX491	Handley Page Jetstream T.1	Instructional airframe

Southampton

Solent Sky Museum
Albert Rd S, Southampton SO14 3FR
www.spitfireonline.co.uk

VH–BRC	Short Sandringham Mk4	Ansett Airlines

Southend

Milton Hall Primary School and Nursery
Salisbury Ave, Westcliffe-on-Sea, Southend-on-Sea, Westcliff-on-Sea SS0 7AU
www.miltonhallschool.com

G–DWJM	Cessna 550 Citation II	Fuselage. Used as a classroom.

Stoke-on-Trent

Kingsland C.E. Academy
Eaves Ln, Werrington, Stoke-on-Trent ST2 8LY
www.kingslandacademy.co.uk

G-SSWE	Short SD3-60-100	Used as a classroom.

Stratford-upon-Avon

Long Marston Airfield
Campden Rd, Stratford-upon-Avon CV37 8LL

G-RACA	Percival Sea Prince T.1	Ex-Royal Navy. In poor condition.

Sunderland

North East Land, Sea & Air Museums
Washington Road, Sunderland SR5 3HZ
www.nelsam.org.uk

G-BEEX	De Havilland DH106 Comet 4B	Cockpit
G-ARPO	Hawker Siddeley HS.121 Trident 1C	Wears false Northeast Airlines colours. Wings and tail to be reattached.
G-OGIL	Short SD3-30-100	Fuselage. Ex-Gill Air.

Warrington

RAF Burtonwood Heritage Centre

c/o Gulivers Kingdom, Warrington WA5 9YZ
www.rafburtonwood.com

N31356	Douglas DC-4	Cockpit

Woodford

Avro Heritage Museum

Chester Rd, Woodford, Stockport SK7 1AG
www.avroheritagemuseum.co.uk

XV235	Hawker Siddeley Nimrod MR.2P	Cockpit
XV106	Vickers VC10 C.1K	Cockpit

Wroughton

Science Museum

Swindon, SN4 9NS

N18E	Boeing 247	
G-ACIT	De Havilland DH84 Dragon	
G-ALXT	De Havilland DH89 Dragon Rapide	Railway Air Services
G-ANAV	De Havilland DH106 Comet 1A	Cockpit
G-APYD	De Havilland DH106 Comet 4B	Dan-Air London
VP975	De Havilland DH104 Devon C2	Royal Air Force
EI-AYO	Douglas C-47A	
G-AWZM	Hawker Siddeley HS.121 Trident 3B	British Airways
N7777G	Lockheed L-749A Constellation	Wears false Trans World Airlines colours.
G-APWY	Piaggio P.166	

Yeovil

Fleet Air Arm Museum
RNAS Yeovilton, Ilchester BA22 8HT
www.fleetairarm.com

G-BSST	Aerospatiale/BAC Concorde	Prototype
WP313	Percival Sea Prince T.1	Royal Navy

York

Yorkshire Air Museum
Halifax Way, Elvington, York YO41 4AU
www.yorkshireairmuseum.org

G-KOOL	De Havilland DH104 Devon C2	Royal Air Force. Marked VP967.
G-AMYJ	Douglas C-47B	Royal Air Force. Marked KN353.
G-AVPN	Handley Page HPR-7 Herald 213	Cockpit
XV250	Hawker Siddeley Nimrod MR.2P	Royal Air Force
XS735	Hawker Siddeley HS.125 Dominie T.1	Fuselage. Ex-Royal Air Force.

Index – Aircraft Types